STO

ALLEN COUNTY PUBLIC LIBRARY

ACPL ITEM
DISCARDED

3 0126 9759

SO-ATG-266

FEB 23 '76

Surgeon
at
Work

CLARENCE J. SCHEIN, M.D.

Surgeon
at
Work

STEIN AND DAY/*Publishers*/New York

First published in 1976
Copyright © 1976 by Clarence J. Schein
All rights reserved
Designed by David Miller
Printed in the United States of America
Stein and Day/*Publishers*/Scarborough House,
Briarcliff Manor, N.Y. 10510

Library of Congress Cataloging in Publication Data

Schein, Clarence J
    Surgeon at work.

    1. Schein, Clarence J. 2. Surgeons—Correspondence,
reminiscences, etc. 3. Surgery. I. Title.
R154.S3533A33   617'.092'4   75-11819
ISBN 0-8128-1836-9

1890475

TO BEN

who added a haven and compassionate ardor

to a canonic voice and fraternal ear.

18304?3

Preface

I am a surgeon, descended from priests, wizards, military wound dressers, bone setters, sow gelders, and barbers. A short time ago we used the services of grave robbers, fought for the bodies of hanged criminals, and operated under the blanket of modesty, and our greatest asset was speed as our patients screamed.

Today we assume the role of the clergyman, profess the erudition of the professional scholar, are as proud of our skill as the virtuoso musician, and accept the reward of the entrepreneur.

Our press is bad. Our fees are exorbitant.

This tells of what it is to be a surgeon in practice.

Surgeon
at
Work

1

It is eight o'clock in the morning and I should have a knife in my hand. But the operation is delayed.

The scrub nurse is there, but she hasn't yet put out her instruments. The chief resident, who is supposed to assist me, is not there at all. Even the patient is still "on the way down."

I try to control my irritability or I'll be as vulnerable to an ulcer as my patient, whose hyperacidity has brought him to the operating table.

My old chief once said, "The only people really involved in an operation are you and the patient. The patient because he has no alternative. You because it's your job. Everybody else is a transient. The residents come and go. The medical students observe and leave. The nurses will eventually get married. If things go well you'll see very little subsequently of your patient, who will probably even forget your name."

Nobody tells me to get up at five-thirty in the morning. But if I don't get up then I don't have time to read the paper before I get to the hospital. If I don't have time to read the paper I won't be able to do it the rest of the day and then I'm dependent on the radio. That's not what I want. I need to know the details of the theater, music, the obituaries, the scientific happenings.

My routine affects everybody around me. Constantly I have to prod the fellow who delivers the newspaper to get my copy to me on time. My family hears too early the hum of the electric shaver, the splash of shower, the pot boiling, even though I try to shut it off before it starts to whistle.

I read the paper with a red pencil, checking off what I want to concentrate upon. I have an ordinary pencil in my pajama pocket because there are things that strike me during the night which I must write down.

One of the best times of the day is the half-hour ride to the hospital, the one completely quiet interval when I'm not available to anyone: not to the reasonable but impossible-to-fulfill demands of the family, patients, office personnel, the hospital. At that hour of the morning there is a program of music and I indulge Walter Mitty visions of myself at the oboe or clarinet in that woodwind quintet.

I park in the underground hospital garage. This facility has been available only recently. It used to be that the first truly challenging event of the morning was to circle the several blocks around the hospital complex in order to find a spot for the car. It had to be in an area suitable for all-day parking. The game was to cruise down the street in anticipation of some parked car's wheels starting to turn out. There would be a lunge to the area like fish in a pool toward new food particles. There were then no garages; the hospital had been built when real estate and space was already too expensive and parking was left to the law of survival. Those who had to come to the hospital would in some way find a place for their cars. For transitory visitors this inconvenience was felt not to matter.

I was lucky. The owner of one of the small private houses nearby parked his own car in front of his home; he drove to work at seven o'clock in the morning. I had waited for him to pull out so often that we had developed a sort of nodding good-morning recognition of each other. Finally, he suggested that he would keep the spot for me on a regular basis if I appeared promptly at seven. He preferred having a doctor's car in front rather than that of an unknown hospital visitor. We got to the point where we exchanged holiday cards. The arrangement worked well for years. Now this man parks all day in front of his own house; there is such a parking problem in the city business area that he now travels by subway.

I walk from the garage to the office with one of several nurses a little late for their seven-to-three-thirty shift. In the office I lay out the day's schedule for my secretary, and put on a white coat with my nameplate over the breast pocket. Professors in a medical school and hospital wear long white coats; it is a professional uniform. I like its deep side pockets because I can carry reading material for the inevitable waiting periods of the day. Seniority in academic rank can be related to the frequency with which these coats are changed and their pristine creases maintained.

Mrs. Ellis has title of assistant administrator and supervisor of the operating room. She had left Jamaica with a nursing scholarship sixteen years ago. She tells me, "You know, you don't come as often anymore to do those 2 A.M. bleeding ulcers and strangulated hernias and accident cases, so you're not as understanding as you used to be about delays. When the girls have been busy all night they just don't have time to set up all the instruments for the next day's cases. Not only that, but Miss Williams, who was going to scrub with you, called in sick. So have a cup of coffee and come back in fifteen minutes. We ought to be ready for you then."

There is no place to get another cup of coffee. The coffee in the nurses' room isn't ready until the whole crew is in and one of them gets a chance to prepare it. I settle for a glass of tomato juice from the can in the utility-room refrigerator.

I try to avoid the doctors' locker room. It's not neat. There are wet towels, bloodstained scrub suits thrown on the floor instead of in the basket, and stained brown-paper lunch bags left behind by the night porters. There are only two chairs and no place to lie down. It's come to be a general concourse and meeting place; once it was an enclave for surgeons alone. The lockers are eight feet high and one foot wide and are designed for two. Sometimes a locker is pilfered. Most of us carry cash in our socks. Some of these "surgeon's tumors" are bulky. This alone could account for the popularity of knee-length stockings in this profession.

I hope my co-tenant is elsewhere. Cramming in two overcoats, a change of shoes, suit, and briefcases hasn't made for neighborliness. And in my case my locker mate also conserves X rays and soiled undershirts. Nor do I want to run into another surgeon, Dr. Fisher. We had never gotten along even when I first encountered him in another hospital. Al Fisher had begun as a pharmacist, which was, to him, second-class status. He went back to the university to fill in requirements and after that graduated from a medical school in Mexico. He remains pathologically thin; a tall figure about whom there is basically something not clean. It isn't just that his clothes are never properly pressed, because that holds true for many of us; and it isn't just that his hair isn't combed. There is an aura about him of general scruffiness. His manner is usually

13

surly and contemptuous. What we share is the prima donna quality most surgeons have. I can never forgive him for behavior which in another field might not be considered so heinous. But once, at a surgical conference, he presented a point of view that directly opposed mine in a subject I'd investigated for two years, and when I asked that he support his contrary opinion by something besides personal prejudice he just waved his hand and said, "Well, everybody knows that," and walked out of the conference. Not much of a reason for perpetual hostility. But surgeons behave that way.

The scrub suits are folded away in bins, one for shirts and the other for trousers. They're labeled large and medium, which in fact turns out to mean too large or too small. They take a lot of abuse. They are not supposed to be worn outside the O.R. but the house staff soon learns that they make adequate pajamas and sweat suits and handy wear between cases. The white ones can be worn outside, the use of green or blue is restricted to the operating room. It is not surprising that the shirts frequently have only one button, so that either the upper chest or the lower abdomen gets exposed. The purse string in the trousers can be too short, or torn, so that they often have to be held up by safety pins like the pajamas of a toddler.

I've had the experience of the trousers falling down to the ankles underneath the operating gown. There is a choice of just stepping out of them or asking one of the nurses to hoist and tie them. There are those who wear nothing under the scrub suit on the principle that there is going to be a certain amount of spill at the scrub sink and during the operative procedure. Blood, water, pus, and saline soak through. Then there is the shy one who not only retains his shorts and undershirt but goes into the adjacent bathroom to change; he is the only one to have his locker equipped with separate hangers for coat, jacket, trousers, and shirt.

Street shoes are not worn in the operating room. In the days of the horsedrawn vehicle there was the danger of manure soiling. The stool of animals contains bacteria that can produce serious infections in humans. These same organisms reside in the soil as the source of tetanus and kindred gangrene-producing infections. The special kind of footwear to be used only in the O.R. runs to soft slippers, wooden clogs, discarded tennis shoes, or simply an old pair of shoes in which the laces have been replaced by an umbilical

14

tape ligature and the sole is so loose as to produce a percussive flap. The fellow with the hangers is the only one I know who changes into shined black shoes. I have developed an attachment to my ancient scuffed pair—we have been through some difficult times together. Over the past ten years I've had only one other pair. The nurses had embarrassed me into discarding them. For me they were adequate despite the loose heel and the lack of full soles and tongues. I should have had a bronze facsimile made as a memento.

I've resisted Mrs. Ellis's suggestion that all personnel wear the same type of shoe which could be purchased at a discount not only because I oppose regimentation but also because the store could then post a "Doctors wear our shoes" notice. A sandwich shop across the street from the hospital displays a sign: "The Doctors Eat Here. Our Food Must Be Good." We go because there is no other place; the food is palatable only by comparison with the unvarying menu of the hospital cafeteria.

One day individuality in attire may be eliminated by the further ingenuity and promotional zeal of the surgical-supply manu-facturers, who are now intent on disposables—use once and throw away. We have it for catheters, intestinal tubes, suture-removal sets, I.V. sets, draping sheet, certain instruments, tracheotomy tubes, and suction catheters. Why not O.R. shoes and undergar-ments and wallet-size stockings?

Not all hospital dressing rooms are the same. I remember visit-ing a surgeon in Switzerland to watch him do an operation for which he was famous. His assistant took me through the operating suite into the general locker room. The lockers, instead of being eight feel tall, were four feet to get twice as much use from the same space. When the operation was over I started back toward the locker room, but the professor steered me in the opposite direction. A diener came out and put a wool blanket over his shoulders.

We then entered a room that was ten by twelve. There was a table with a pot of steaming coffee and two cold glasses of orange juice and several cookies. There was also a couch. This was the locker room reserved for the professor. Here we could converse privately until the deferential orderly came to notify the professor that the next case was ready. He changed trousers and shirt between cases. This is the only time I have ever seen freshly laundered,

15

beautifully pressed operating-room attire with the monogrammed initials of the surgeon over the breast pocket. By these things are the few remaining surgical emperors recognizable.

All our operating rooms come off a common corridor. My case was scheduled for room D. I peered into the window from the hallway and could see that the patient had just been moved from the stretcher onto the operating table. This hospital now has fourteen operating rooms. There was a time when there were only two operating rooms and two kinds of operations: those that were brain operations and those that weren't.

I walked in to say hello to Mr. Padget because mine would be the only face he would recognize. He was lying in the ultimate trusting passivity of a man who was soon to have his abdomen opened and worked on by people he did not know, whose competence he could be assured of through no testing of his own. His main concern had been my promise to introduce the stomach tube under anesthesia; he had become phobic about this from his last hospital experience. He nodded to me through the drowsiness of his preanesthetic medication.

A dark-skinned Indian lady resident in anesthesiology stretched Padget's arm out on a board and tied it in position. Her name was Patel; she had a rouged red spot on her forehead. She showed her experience by shaving the patient's forearm of its thick hair; otherwise the adhesive for the tubing would not stick. A rubber tourniquet above the elbow was held taut by a surgical clamp which releases more easily than the old slipknot. "Open and close your fist," she said softly. Her voice was comforting. Some residents are bored with the setting in of an intravenous line; they can be laconic or rough. Padget's veins stood out like those on Michelangelo's Moses.

Patel used the sharp number 18 needle to puncture the skin at an angle; then threaded the needle into the vein. Five ml. of blood was aspirated into the syringe. (This terminology has replaced the old cc.; we're all going continental.) This is the anesthetist's security for typing and cross match should a transfusion be necessary. She threaded a transparent plastic tube into the lumen of the needle and into the vein. The needle is removed from the vein and catches on to the end of the plastic tube as the female fit for the outlet of the

16

liter of glucose and water that is hanging from the hook of the six-foot pole.

The resident is too young to know, but there was a time when the needles were reused. A woman in the supply unit operated a pump that would blow the lumen clean and the needle was then dropped into an autoclave for sterilization. Each needle would then be packed in sterile gauze and rubber-banded into a number 18 needle pack. Now needles are used once and discarded. It is more efficient, less likely to be contaminated, and said to be cheaper.

This intravenous line is also the avenue for drugs that serve to relax the abdominal muscles. Patel had learned to smile quietly at the surgeon's impatience to begin, knowing how upset he would be if the patient's muscles tightened during the procedure. Padget probably did not care that the chemical basis for relaxing had its origins in the paralyzing arrowheads tipped with a curare used by South American Indians.

Dr. Lacey, the attending anesthetist, now appeared. Lacey was plump and spoke with a faint lisp. He was a bright man and interested in his patients. "I.V. in O.K.? Let's put him under." And, to the patient, "I'm Dr. Lacey. I'm going to put you to sleep. When you wake up it will be all over and you will be in the recovery room. Dr. Patel, please start the pentothal drip. Good night, Mr. Padget." Padget began to snore, until they extended his neck. His eyeballs stopped moving and the first stage of anesthesia had been accomplished.

They were now going to insert an endotracheal tube that would pass oxygen and other gases to the lungs. It now seems such an obvious and simple concept, this way of controlling the respiratory environment. But we didn't have it fifty years ago. Those operations requiring it had then to be done in specially regulated pressure chambers where the patient was in one set of atmospheric conditions and the staff in another. We stand on the shoulders of the past. I don't know who actually first devised this tube, but its antecedent required the capacity to see the vocal cords. The tube has to be positioned between the vocal cords and just below them.

It was a voice coach for opera singers who developed the first mirror system to see the larynx. Now they used a specially curved self-contained battery-operated laryngoscope. Patel was to insert

17

the tube. She was as organized and unhurried about it as she had been about the I.V. She removed the comma-shaped mouth gag that prevented the patient from biting his tongue. She inspected his teeth. She knew that she would have to be careful about the porcelain jackets over the central and lateral incisors. The left lower partial denture had been removed by the floor nurse, and noted on the O.R. checklist.

Dr. Patel, with Lacey standing by and assuming responsibility, put the scope in over the patient's tongue and pushed up the base to see the epiglottis. As it was elevated by the tip of the scope, a hot puff of air came through the vocal cords. She slipped in the endotracheal tube which Lacey handed her, and then fixed it into position with adhesive. The patient was now relaxed and being ventilated through the tube.

"We're ready, Dr. Schein."

Meanwhile, Mrs. Rodriguez, functioning as scrub nurse in the absence of Miss Williams, was arranging the instrument table and Mayo stand. She was forty, and sturdy, overweight, scrubbing usually only to instruct the nurses in the tech school.

Each surgeon uses some special tools. This is taken into consideration and the O.R. supervisor keeps a list of preferences. In the early years my list varied so much that this was an appropriate excuse for not having it always available. Now it changes rarely.

The special instruments have minor features that make them useful, and sometimes indispensable. Often a particular curve, angle or tooth or length is called for. Such details make a difference.

For example, in intestinal surgery I find numbered small clothespins a good way to label serial sutures. A soup ladle is good for catching spilled gallstones; a tablespoon is a good retractor for closing the peritoneum; a teaspoon wedged into a steel rod offers an extra long finger. These are the many details that Williams knows, and that Rodriguez will quickly remember.

Mrs. Rodriguez and I are old friends. I said, "It's nice to see you working again," and she answered, "Please behave. I may not immediately remember all your special things, and since when do you refuse the plastic suckers and insist on the old metal tonsil suction that we'd discard if it weren't for you?"

"I use it because it works. Like you and me, Rodriguez, getting not younger doesn't mean getting older."

18

"O.K. I'm ready. Where is your crew? It's almost eight-fifteen."

Assistants coming late has to do with the descent of the surgeon from Olympus. The attending surgeon in former times was frock-coated, aloof, generally wealthy and influential, and his subordinates were totally dependent on his whim and good will for the opportunity to learn the techniques, let alone have a place to practice them. Positions were few and available for virtues that often had very little to do with merit or promise. Surgery was a hierarchy, the blade passed on to those in the small coterie about the chief or department head.

After the Second World War surgeons were no longer gods. They were just people who had had the opportunity to learn. It was cruel in my day: how did we tolerate fifteen dollars a month, on call two out of three nights, forbidden to marry, no women allowed in the house staff quarters?

Although surgeons of my generation take a perverse pride in the way we were forced to work, and decry the softer conditions of today's salaries and privileges, we recognize this new justice.

One of the residents had said that he didn't think it necessary to be quite so compulsive about starting on time since, in the history of this patient or in the context of his own life or mine, what difference did it make? Medically, he might have a point. But this attitude misses the role of discipline in surgery, which means exact attention to details. The difference in exactness is a major difference in surgeons. It's not proper in surgery nor in music to do something that's a little bit less accurate than it ought to be. A musician would not play C where a C sharp is called for. Musicians say that to the skilled ear there is a difference in the tonality of the same note written as C sharp or D flat. The superior surgeon, or the surgeon who makes fewest errors, believes that there are no minor details. He has to have some obsessive and compulsive characteristics. Mother Nature is a bitch and if things can go wrong they will.

Speed, surgical heroics, and display may have been required in the days before adequate anesthesia and fluid replacement. It may then have been necessary to do an amputation in fifty-eight seconds. Most of those patients died from blood loss, infection, or shock. Now we can work with an exactness and attention to infinite detail that is the art of surgery as distinct from the craft of the military surgeons of the past. Part of this compulsive approach is

19

the need to do things when they're called for, which means being on time.

I had put on my mask and was starting to scrub when my assistants walked in. The chief resident, Paul Spector, had been detained by an emergency admission, and Newman, the third-year medical student, had been assigned to the case only ten minutes ago. It was hard to rebut such excuses. We started to scrub; each of us had a separate sink. Three faucets running virtually full force for ten minutes. You figure out the number of gallons of water required to scrub one operating team.

There is a tendency always to scrub less than the required ten minutes and it is the experienced nurse who will come up behind you as you start to walk from the scrub room. "But, Dr. Schein, look at the clock, you've only scrubbed six minutes." You smile guiltily and go back and do it for another three.

The abdomen is cleaned and prepared, which means it is given the same soap-and-water scrubbing as our hands. It is then painted with an iodinelike compound. The entire abdomen is covered except for the area where the incision is to be made, a strip of skin from just below the breastbone down to the belly button and the shaved area of the pubis. The abdominal wall, so exposed and draped, has no distinctive personality. Here we are all alike.

We are at the table, I on the right, the first assistant, Paul Spector, opposite me, and the medical student, Newman, standing to my left. Nurse Rodriguez is at lower left facing me. I nod to the anesthetist. She nods back. We are ready. The nurse hands me the knife.

I make the incision through the skin beginning just below the end of the breastbone and extending down to the belly button and then through the middle of the belly button to a point two inches below it. There was a time when the belly button was regarded as sanctified. The ancients called it the umbilicus—meaning the center or beginning. We made every effort to preserve it. The gynecologist especially would make curved incisions around the umbilicus to maintain its virginal contours. Later I will sew up the umbilicus so you can't tell it has been bisected.

In this area the abdominal muscles and tissues have so fused together that there are only a few blood vessels. Here I can effect a rapid entrance into the abdomen with the minimum blood loss. The assistant and I have put our hands on opposite sides of the abdominal wall and as the incision goes through the skin this separates and falls to each side pulling away from the midline. Here the underlying fat has a particularly bright yellow color which is distinctive from the fat of the rest of the abdominal wall as the light in Athens is different from the light in Rome.

The incision goes through the fat. The bleeding spots are grasped with a small clamp and an electric current is used to coagulate. The surgeon hears a buzz and a small area of charring occurs—a pinpoint burn. This is a rapid way of controlling bleeding and the burned spot is of no consequence. The incision is further deepened to come down on the thin membrane that holds the abdominal organs in place. It is called the peritoneum, from the Greek *peri* meaning around, and *tenere* to hold. This fine membrane is picked up with two opposing forceps held by me and my assistant. I then carefully nick the membrane with a scalpel and put my finger through the small opening and extend the incision up and down. The bowel starts to protrude, part of the liver jerks out, and we're in the belly.

2

Charles Newman was one of the six third-year medical students assigned to me for his surgical clerkship. He had completed his three-month exposures to obstetrics and gynecology and medicine. This was his first experience with a stomach operation. He still bore some adolescent acne which he hoped to counter with a short black mustache.

I said, "The first thing you do after you open a belly, Newman, is not to touch but to look."

"I'm looking," he said.

"What do we know? The patient has an ulcer. But how can we be sure that's the true reason for his symptoms? Could he have developed a tumor in the meantime? Could he have adhesions? Could he have something else? You just can't be sure in advance."

"So we look," the student said, almost losing his balance as he peered under the rib cage.

I asked an orderly to bring him a stool to stand on.

"Let's begin by looking away from where we think the trouble is, and work toward it. Let's go first to the lower abdomen. To expose it, we lift up the transverse colon—that's this, the part of the large intestine that goes from right to left at about the level of the umbilicus. You take it now and lift it."

Newman said, "What?"

"Place your fingers on either end and lift it."

Charles Newman, who knew he was going to be a doctor, reached in and for the first time in his life was holding on to a piece of a living person's intestine.

"Hand the colon to me, I'll hold it while you feel these little lumps. What do you think they are?"

22

Newman put his hand in timidly. "Tumors?"

"Spector," I said, "tell him what it is."

Paul Spector, chief resident, on his way out into private practice, smiled behind his mask. "How often has the colon been opened for this kind of 'tumor,' Dr. Schein?"

"Unfortunately, more than once. Tell the lad, Paul."

"They're pieces of stool."

"Right."

"What shall we look at now, Newman?" I said.

"I have no idea."

"Good. Medical students shouldn't have opinions. What do you think, Paul?"

"I guess we'd better be sure the colon is okay."

"Right." I traced the rest of the large bowel between my fingers and followed it down to the point where it curves around the spleen and the left kidney and gets down to the pelvic area. All of this was normal, no tumor, no evidence of inflammation.

"O.K., now let's run the small bowel."

What this means is that you hold this inch-wide velvety tube between your fingers and inch along it like a garden hose. What you feel is as important as what you see.

"What's always bothered me," Newman said, "is how do you tell just where the small intestine begins."

As I did it I said, "You put your hand in all the way to the back until you can feel the spine on the left side. Then curve your finger around and you'll be touching it. That's the beginning of the small bowel, which is called the jejunum, from the word meaning dull, insipid, or empty because early anatomists saw no food in it."

"Hey," Paul Spector said, "this guy's got a Meckel's diverticulum."

Medical students remember it by the twos. It is two inches long, occurs in two percent of the population, and occurs two inches from the end of the small intestine. This is a kind of second appendix. It can get inflamed and painful and people who have had their appendices removed get an attack of simulated appendicitis.

"Now if Paul will pull up on the costal margin to get the ribs out of the way we can take a look at the liver."

It was smooth, without evidence of fatty changes, which was only a little amazing considering how much I knew Padget drank.

"Tell me, Paul, how much alcohol do you need to get changes in the liver?"

"I know that," Newman said. "I saw it in the *Times*. One drink can do it."

"They were quoting from the *New England Journal of Medicine*," Spector said. "If you should happen to be a drinker who goes to a doctor who doesn't read either the *Times* or the *New England Journal of Medicine*, then you know more about it than he does."

"Newman, any comments?"

"I don't want to change the subject, Dr. Schein, but does it always look like this, the belly?"

For the student this experience was finally joining him to the profession. Now it was not pictures in textbooks, or dogs in the lab, or slides in lectures or formalin-pickled organs in crocks. When I was a medical student the operating room was impenetrable. There was no window. The entrance was guarded. No third-year student ever got inside—unless you took a surgical elective, in which case you ran around the hospital delivering bloods and urines to the laboratory, chased down pathology reports, changed stinking dressings on gangrenous feet, did blood counts and urines at two o'clock in the morning, and for all that scut work you were permitted to peek over the shoulder of some staff man to watch a procedure. At the time surgery was a postgraduate discipline. The closest students ever came to an operation was in the amphitheater.

Those of us in the gallery could see nothing more than the backs of those at the operating table. There is an oil painting by Eakins of the clinic of Dr. Agnew in Philadelphia which shows this.

"Dr. Schein, I understand you are king of the gallbladder and emperor of the common duct. Could you please point out those organs?"

"Newman, who wised you up to say that?" I pretended to frown, but answered, "The gallbladder is here, on the undersurface of the liver. You have to turn the liver up a bit to see it. It doesn't look completely normal now. It ought to be robin's-egg blue and virtually transparent, but the reaction around it has come from the adjacent ulcer. If you'll be gentle I'll let you feel it. Are there stones in it?"

24

"I don't feel any," Newman said, sounding a little breathless.

"Like feeling for pebbles in a balloon filled with water. However, we do know that an X ray taken three weeks ago showed this gallbladder to be normal. Spector, you're just a couple of months away from private practice. Is it your opinion that every lady who belches a lot and says she can't eat fatty foods and ice cream and Chinese food ought to have her gallbladder out?"

"Well, Dr. Schein, if I were taking the exam for the American Board of Surgery I would say that only the diseased gallbladder that has stones in it should be removed. I would also say that as far as we know excessive passing of gas and fatty-food intolerance has nothing to do with the gallbladder. That's what I would tell the board examiner. But I tell you, Dr. Schein, that in the four years I've been here I've seen patients with gallbladder symptoms that have been relieved by removing the organ even though that gallbladder looked normal. Apparently there are some diseases of the gallbladder that are unrelated to stones. What the French call *dyskinesias.* I know you're going to ask if I think the gallbladder can have a headache or a neurosis or a migraine attack. Maybe they can. I don't think we know."

"There are doctors who think the way you do, Spector, which might account for the fact that next to the hysterectomy, it's the most common abdominal operation, maybe 750,000 done each year in this country. It's costly. It takes a surgeon about an hour and the fees run from three hundred dollars to a thousand. That's a lot of money to make in an hour and you can understand the resentment of someone who pays that kind of money and doesn't get better, because up to 30 percent find their symptoms incompletely relieved. You could understand the resentment even if the patient did get better. And you know what happens to the symptoms in some 'successful' cases? They're shifted to the bowel and we see colitis, or to the heart and we see shortness of breath and palpitations. Because the complaints were neurotic to begin with. I tell you, Paul Spector, you can send a symptom from your head to your gallbladder as you can from your head to your genitals. Don't be fooled into taking out a gallbladder when the symptoms might be coming from personality problems."

Spector shrugged, unconvinced.

"Newman." I said, "you have any opinions on this?"

25

"I learned the five F's—fat, fertile, flatulent female of forty. But you see the disease in men, don't you?"

"Of course. But back to Mr. Padget. Mrs. Rodriguez, a lap pad please, folded in half, and one in thirds, one Harrington retractor, and one Deaver. Lap pad under the liver and the Harrington over it to expose the duodenum. Now the other retractor up on the left side of the falciform ligament, which holds the liver to—to what, Dr. Newman?"

"To the abdominal wall?"

"Amazingly correct. Now we swing it all up to see the right side of the stomach. We get the omentum off—it was placed here to close off the previous perforation—and now we'll be able to see the ulcer itself, but before we commit ourselves we better take another good look!"

26

3

The old man used to say that the only surgical procedure to be done in the office was to put on a bandage that doesn't slip. My office is now in a separate building, it is part of the hospital where I work. My hours are in the morning, after rounds at the hospital, and before luncheon case conferences. The office is mainly for talking and listening to people. Listening tells you the diagnosis. There are things you shouldn't ask. Like where the clergyman picked up gonorrhea, or why the businessman wants to pay cash, or why the suburban lady is accompanied by her friend rather than her husband.

The office is where the results of your operations are brought in for your evaluation. This is where you judge yourself. Satisfaction comes from seeing patients, in a prolonged follow-up, whose problems have been alleviated. It is rare to see really sick patients in the office; the acutely ill go directly to the hospital.

I've Scotch-taped two playing cards, a four of clubs and an ace of hearts, to my office wall and nobody has noticed it, not the students or the patients. It is significant to me alone. The four of clubs in its commonality stands for man's vulnerability, while the ace of hearts is the individual trembling. I don't want practice to immunize me against the fear and despair of the people who come to me as patients. I now confine my activities to the area of abdominal surgery, even though like all young surgeons I once felt equal to any surgical problem involving the skin and its contents.

Dr. Jordan, a gastroenterologist, had called about Sol Padget. He had been involved with Padget's ulcer from the beginning. "There's no possibility of further treating him effectively with drugs

27

and diet. He won't go back to his psychiatrist—too much resistance. His ulcer is scarred down so much now that the stomach contents don't go through; he's starting to retain food and vomit overflow. I think you have to do him soon, before he becomes totally obstructed."

Medical men are reluctant to surrender chronic ulcer patients to surgeons. Mostly when you get the ulcer patient off cigarettes and liquor and onto bed rest he gets better. But the man with an ulcer has a million more acid-producing cells than the normal. Given the same stress provocation, the disease usually recurs. The ulcer patient is at the mercy of his own acidity.

Eight years before this I had received the first call from Dr. Jordan telling me he had a Padget in the emergency room with a perforated ulcer. It was spring. Most ulcers—and nobody knows why—perforate in the spring. Padget had severe abdominal pain; I found boardlike rigidity of his abdomen, and the X ray showed air under the diaphragm. There was no question of the diagnosis. His hyperacidity had punctured through the few remaining cells roofing the hole in his duodenum. I operated, plugged the hole.

Four years after that I got a phone call from a hospital in Canada. It was Padget, saying he had a recurrence of the same symptoms and asking should he come home at once. I said I thought it was probably an emergency and should be taken care of there. Later I got a copy of the hospital record; they had also closed a perforated duodenal ulcer. Now, eight years after I had operated on him, he was coming to see me again.

He arrived to the minute, probably as a result of his psychiatrist's conditioning. He was grayer, pudgier, sloppier in dress, and he looked sick. He looked like a man who was tired of feeling sick.

"I was thinking of calling you before this, Dr. Schein, but Dr. Jordan took me over and I didn't need you."

"You sound a little truculent," I said.

"I'm pretty sick of doctors, if you want to know."

"I don't blame you. Sit down and tell me about it. What's been going on?"

"I haven't got any pain, but I just can't keep food down. The smallest meal blows me up, my breath stinks, and I feel jittery all the time. Why the hell is my ulcer so unusual it has to be operated on over and over? Lots of people have ulcers."

"I'll tell you about that in a minute. First we take a look." In the examining room I could percuss out a greatly distended stomach full of gas and undigested food. He kept belching and spitting, often a vomiting equivalent. The X rays he had brought with him showed that almost none of the swallowed barium had gone through. A small trickle showed an area of narrowing due to scarring.

"Get dressed, Mr. Padget, and we'll talk in the office."

After we were seated I said, "There are about twenty million people in this country who have, had, or will have ulcers. Three out of a hundred doctors are part of that group. Almost all of these people get intermittently better. You happen to be in the small group who have to be treated by operation, even though your original ulcer has healed."

"Healed? Then what the hell's going on?"

"The first two times your ulcer perforated. Now, although the ulcer is healed, that area has been so scarred that it is preventing your food from going through. That's why you've been vomiting."

"I'm sick of Jordan's diet, his antacid pills, his no smoking and no liquor and plenty of rest. And his telling me to stop worrying. He's prescribing a way of life I can't follow. And what the hell does he know about my problems? He sent me to a shrink who knows even less. At a dollar a minute, whether I show up or not, he should have accomplished something. I don't want to hear that I get pains because my mother's tits never satisfied my infant needs. You know what I think, Doctor? I think none of you know a hell of a lot about ulcers. Do I need another operation, and what's going to be different about this one?"

"You've had a hole plugged twice and both were emergency procedures. Each time the ulcer was left where it was. Now we either have to take it out or so fix it that you can't have any more trouble."

"But what about the risk?"

"You want an honest answer?"

"Can I get one?"

"I'll try. You're in good general condition, your heart and

lungs are okay, except for the ulcer Jordan's given you a clean bill. Ninety percent of patients like you have no problem."

"I'm not sure those odds are good enough. If I survive, will I be able to live like a normal person, will I be able to eat normally and so on?"

"Another ninety percent, with accent on eating normally. You can't become a glutton."

"Fair enough. Now tell me what's your fee?"

"That has to depend on what I have to do, and I can't really decide until I'm actually there."

"Okay. Tell me when you want me at the hospital. Meanwhile, can I use your phone? I want to tell that egghead psychiatrist to look for a different sucker."

4

The beginner in surgery invents new variations on old errors. To a bright intern doing his first case I remarked, "Ordinarily there are twelve hazardous steps in the operation. You've discovered four more that I thought couldn't be made."

I don't believe you have to make each error yourself in order to learn. I was teaching a resident to do a thyroidectomy. The operation required that the blood supply to the gland be controlled by tying its medium-sized artery. "Just get underneath it, free it up all around, and pass a ligature around it."

"Dr. Schein, let me cut it first and see it bleed so I know what I shouldn't be doing."

I was aghast, because he meant it. It's not necessary to repeat the errors of the past. Each surgical apprentice shouldn't have to fill his own cemetery in order to learn. The art of surgery also consists in avoiding mistakes.

"Details," I said to Newman and Spector. "Infinite attention to details. Both of you have examined this patient. A third has written up the history. In this room we have also a circulating nurse, a resident anesthetist, and an attending. There is an orderly who has brought the patient in. Is there anybody here who knows the color of the patient's eyes?"

Nobody answered.

"Sherlock Holmes was modeled on Dr. Joseph Bell of Edinburgh, who was famous for his ability to observe and make deductions from the minutiae the untrained never see. Mainly we get this from the patient's own account of himself. The first thing to do in examing a surgical patient is not to lay hands on his abdomen but to pull up a chair and talk to him. He'll tell you in lay terms what

31

you will transfer into a two- or three-word diagnosis. Remember, if he describes something that waddles on webbed feet and quacks, the diagnosis, based on your superior intelligence, is that it is a duck."

"I have to remember that," Newman said.

"Why not?" I said. "I remember it from the guy who first told it to me. Now let's look at this ulcer in some greater detail."

I stood at the operating table and saw myself in three parts. Newman was myself twenty-five years ago. Spector was yesterday.

Newman came from a family of musicians and he had wanted to be one himself. His grandfather, who had learned to play the clarinet in the Russian army, came to this country to be a performer, then a conductor, and then a manager of other orchestras. He heard Newman play the violin and told his mother that the boy ought to become a doctor. It was not a direct progression. In college Newman became interested in medieval German literature and from there to the dramas of Schiller. Schiller had turned from medicine to literature. Newman went in the opposite direction.

Newman arrived for his medical-school interview one-half hour early. He had allowed time to get lost in the maze of buildings. It was his way. There was one other person in the anteroom, sitting on the couch. She was of medium height, soft long brown hair, well combed, frank open face, thin long crossed legs, suntanned, with cashmere sweater and plaid skirt and flat shoes. There was a one-inch scar under the right jaw. He noticed the stockings were taut and perfectly aligned. Her casual air contrasted with his anxiety. She was smoking a cigarette and looked up easily from the newspaper. He had already marked the gulf between them. He couldn't read a newspaper under these circumstances—that is really read it; to hold it was something else.

"Hello," she said. "I'm Cathy Forge. What time are you scheduled for?"

Newman, "Three-fifteen."

"Well, then, I'm ahead of you."

Then the door opened and one of the secretaries came out.

"Miss Forge, would you please come in?"

He was alone in the waiting room. Twenty minutes later Cathy came out. "Relax. it's not bad." Was his nervousness so apparent? The secretary called him in.

There were two interviewers: one in a white coat, and the other in a business suit. They represented the ad hoc committee on admissions, one from the full-time faculty and the other a clinician in practice who gave part of his time to the university. The names of the members of the committee were never revealed, and the committee members were changed every academic year so that there would be no pressure on them. They introduced themselves, the white-coated as an associate professor in the Department of Pharmacology, and the other as an associate clinical professor of medicine. "Mr. Newman, we have gone over your application, and we are aware of your academic record. We want to tell you about the problems that the admissions committee are faced with. We have 126 places open for this coming year and for each place there are ten applications. Of these ten applications about two are not acceptable for consideration by virtue of their previous academic record. About 5 percent of those applying already have Ph.D.'s in engineering, chemistry, or math. We are seeing more people wanting to be doctors who for one reason or another have decided to give up fields in which a doctorate was already acquired. One out of every four of those admitted will be a woman. That gives you the background. We think you should know that 10 percent of those admitted will give up within the first year, finding that they have made a wrong choice. Tell us why you want to be a doctor."

At this point Newman could see little point in the interview; there was nothing that wasn't in the application. All they wanted was to see what he looked like, and how he handled himself.

"I have always believed that I would be happiest if I could do something with my hands and with my brain that would in some way serve two purposes: the first that it would be of value to somebody else and the second that it would be interesting to me. I believe that both of these goals can be fulfilled by being a doctor. I also think that medicine would give me some sort of personal independence."

The one with the white coat said, "What made you choose this particular medical school?"

Newman thought this might be the stinker. He had heard of one

33

school where one of the legs on the chair in which the interviewee sat was purposely cut one-half inch short so that the chair would rock; those who were observing were interested in seeing the reaction this produced. The interview version of the laboratory experiments of people under stress.

"Because of its good reputation."

The white-coated man asked if Newman had any questions.

Newman said, "No."

They said, "Thank you very much for coming here today," and one of them escorted him to the door. There were two more candidates waiting. Ten days later an envelope with the university's name in the upper left-hand corner arrived.

There was no point in hesitating about opening it. The first three words solved the problem: "We are pleased." His father sent off the first semester's tuition, he called up the other two schools to which he had applied to withdraw his application, and for the first time in his life he felt an unencumbered happiness.

In the operating room the circulating nurse was now adjusting the overhead light to beam directly into the operating field. It takes some skill to position this light accurately. It means getting over the shoulders and between the heads of those looking into a narrow field.

Now the area about the ulcer could be seen. The stomach itself was greatly distended and its wall was enormously thickened. Newman said he couldn't see an ulcer.

"That's because it's no longer active. What we are seeing now is the effect of ulcer healing. What happened the first time was that he formed an ulcer so fast that it burst through his stomach. In other words, he 'blew his top,' in his stomach. A good way to think about it.

"This destructive reaction occurred so rapidly that the normal process of healing could not occur. It was too fast. At that time he got a peritonitis, I operated. I sealed the opening. Then it occurred a second time, and the second surgeon did the same thing. Now he has come back with a scar narrowing the passageway connecting the stomach to the intestines.

"Normally there is a valve between the stomach and the small intestine, but it isn't always effective. Sometimes this valve allows forward-going intestinal contents to regurgitate back into the stomach. It is postulated that one of the ways by which ulcers are formed is related to this valve's incompetence. We don't know that this is so. Many people have an incompetent valve and don't have an ulcer. In surgery just as in everything else, there is no always, no never.

"You notice that there is now very little in the way of acute inflammation. You learned that the signs of infection are redness, pain, heat, and swelling—in Latin, *rubor, dolor, calor,* and *tumor.* You can't tell about pain under anesthesia. There is no angry infection here. This scar is the late effect of the previous disease. There is only one ulcer here, and it is on the surface of the duodenum. When an ulcer burrows from the back of the duodenum it penetrates into the pancreas. The pancreas is up against the back and that is why these people get a backache. Newman, do you remember anything about the anatomy of the stomach and pancreas?"

"Well, Dr. Schein, I don't really know the answer to that except that I could answer you with a story."

"O.K., go ahead." **1890475**

"At our college there was a man who taught ancient civilization. He used to give a single examination question at the end of the first two weeks. It was always the same: name the twelve tribes of Israel. The fraternity got to know about this question and in the first two weeks the only thing they memorized was the twelve tribes of Israel. This leaked out to the old gentleman, so with the next class the examination question was to name twelve ancient cities that were engaged in commerce. One fellow answered the examination question by saying, 'Dear Professor, I don't know the names of the twelve cities that were involved in commerce, but here are the twelve tribes of Israel.' Well, Dr. Schein, I don't know the pancreas's relation to the duodenal ulcer, except that it gets involved in it, but I can tell you that the pancreas is the sexiest organ in the body because its head lies in the arms of the duodenum, its body is in the bed of the stomach, and it pokes its tail into the hilum of the spleen."

"Now that we have established that," I said, "here is a man who is forty-seven years of age, who has had an ulcer perforate twice. Now he has an obstruction. There are two ways in which we can handle this. One is to take the ulcer out and rid him of it, the simplistic biblical approach of removing the offending part. The second way is to so readjust his gastric physiology that we will bypass the effects of the obstructed ulcer and at the same time prevent a new ulcer from forming, or so we hope.

"Spector, you are supposed to be up on all of the latest information. You have read next month's journals. How do you reason out what our approach should be? Give me facts, the figures, and the numbers, the percentages, and the mortality rates and the morbidity rates, the percentages of cures. Start by telling us the logic for either operation."

5

Four years before this, after reviewing Paul Spector's application for a residency, I was interviewing him on a Saturday morning. He had come in on terminal leave from the Air Force. Still in uniform and paratrooper boots, he was tall enough to make my five eight uncomfortable. His hair, short even by military standards, was growing back in a light brown fullness. He had the main ingredient for a surgeon—energy—and he had the untroubled look of a man who had made up his mind about where he wanted to go and how to get there.

He came from a small western town where his father is in general practice. At medical school in Chicago he was in the middle third scholastically but had been elected permanent vice-president. After interning he had gone back to join his father's practice, and that had been interrupted by two years in the service. Now he had thought out his decision not to devote his medical life to his father's type of practice.

"My father still has a role in his community. He does hernias, fractures, appendectomies. But he is in under the grandfather clause—the new people will have to be board-certified. But no matter how you dress it up it's still general practice. Soon there won't be doctors like my father; increasingly the medical stuff is going to be taken care of by superspecialists or by paramedical people and nurses. I don't want to be easily disposable, and I want to make my own decisions about which medical problems I want to be involved with. I would rather operate than give pills. I don't want a practice with patients most of whom would get better by themselves, or keep referring them to specialists who would send me a copy of their operative reports, and a note to feel free to visit

37

the patient in the hospital. The Air Force convinced me you've got to have the piece of paper in order to get anywhere."

"Is that all you want—that official seal in the corner and the business about 'having satisfactorily demonstrated' and so on? Is that worth five years of sweat?"

It was as if he had anticipated the question and had the answer prepared. "I've got to be practical about it. I believe that in my time, in one way or another, the government is going to take over the practice of medicine. I didn't like this state of affairs in the Air Force, I don't expect to like it in my private life, but I think it's coming and I want to prepare for it. Paper accreditation will be one way of deciding who is to do what, and maybe eventually who is to go where. I want to work in a hospital, not be part of an outpatient clinic. I want to be part of a surgical team, not on a family health-maintenance program. I want to do something that non-physician personnel cannot be taught in a two-year crash program. I don't want to be a replaceable spare part."

"Suppose you're wrong," I said.

"Oh, I could be wrong. It may be that family doctor turns out to be the kingpin, because he will have control of the patient, and especially if he organizes he may be able to do this without killing himself with impossible hours and endless telephone calls. Also, although most specialists go directly into training after medical school, I've already served my time in private practice. Between that and the Air Force I've done my part. I know what I don't want."

Although I didn't think this applicant was ever going to make any original contribution to the science of surgery, he would probably, because of his purposefulness and direction, be an asset to any hospital as a practical bread-and-butter surgeon. And we already had more than enough professors. He would be trained and leave, and we wanted that. The ones who, for reasons of scholarship and academic proficiency, we would want to stay—those we would seek out and select. So I found Spector suitable. Unfortunately there would be a year's hiatus before an opening could be found for him.

"There isn't a slot for you now. It'll take a year. Are you willing to wait?"

"Sure, I expected something like that. I'll go back and work with the old man, build up my bank account. There's a wife and child to consider."

In a way I envied Spector, his directness, his practicality, even his opportunity to become a country doctor, something I had always wanted for myself without being able to force myself to relinquish the presumed scholastic advantages of big-city involvement. "Meanwhile, how about some reading, at least some things you ought to look at. To get you back into the vocabulary. Maingot's *Abdominal Operations*. And you ought to look through the last couple of years of the surgical journals."

"Sure," he said, and I felt that he would.

"And one other thing. Find the time to review the new stuff on surgical physiology with special attention to fluid balance, cardiovascular and pulmonary function, and the physiology of digestion. This will bring you up to date; that time in the Air Force had to take you away from the special and basic problems of surgery."

A year later he put his family into a small suburban house twelve miles from the hospital and started his residency. On night duty he was content to stay in the on-call room at the hospital and pass his time in the intensive care unit. What he was interested in, he made clear, was bread-and-butter surgery. Where he intended to practice would not provide him with elaborate facilities. "I'll send the big stuff to you professors. I don't want complications. I want happy patients. Stomachs, colons, gallbladders, breasts, uteri, and varicose veins. You can take the tumors of the pancreas and liver."

The esoteric lectures on unusual subjects he managed to avoid. "I don't care about subtle footnotes, ratology, or operations on guinea pigs." He pronounced "academic scholarship" with a different final consonant.

He thought much of scholarship could be replaced with common sense. I knew he was wrong. He had yet to learn that ignorance meant committing avoidable errors and the failure to recognize correctable conditions.

As a second- and third-year resident Spector was, I felt, responsible and available. He knew his cases. He never felt it beneath his dignity to remove sutures, to do routine dressings, or to restart an I.V. He was not above replacing an orderly in wheeling a patient to the X-ray department. His light touch and wholesome maturity (he was several years older than the usual resident) endeared him to the nurses, who knew he would not slough off an onerous triviality with a request that the intern be called.

He did one thing I liked. He addressed patients as Mr., Miss, and Mrs., unlike the other staff people, who went quickly to first names. The patient might come in as a Mr. but a day after the operation he became Joe. My own feeling is that if a doctor has worked for his title, and he doesn't himself like to be first-named, in the same way a patient has worked for his own title. Hospitals have a tendency to depersonalize.

He stamped each of his patients' nameplates onto a three-by-five card and along with that the date of operation, important blood findings, or X-ray information; and those social facts—relative to be notified and so on—so that he would have the data at a glance. He kept a batch of these on his person, shuffling them about as he made rounds. The discharged patients' records he retained in a shoe box, so that they could always be referred to later as reminders of specific operations and treatment.

It used to be that we had to write everything out. Given the largely apocryphal indictment of doctors' handwriting, patients were not always identified as well as they might have been. Now the plate, with the patient's name and social security number, is used to stamp each page of his chart and each laboratory and accounting slip.

Each division of surgery has its own color index card. Spector perverted that and correlated the color with the disease—green for gallbladder and liver, yellow for stomach, red for vascular, brown for colon and intestine, white for miscellaneous. Younger members of the staff copied his system. It was one of his legacies, and a resident could always be known by his bulging pockets. Another reason Spector is remembered is by the sudden nature and aftermath of his illness.

It occurred during one of those T.G.I.F. nights, the lull before the weekend, toward the end of the first year as resident. In the staff quarters Spector dominated the conversation to the accompaniment of salami, clams, and beer. He had endless anecdotes about community practice, coloring it so that the younger people gave him much of the attention they had once given to *Arrowsmith* and *Microbe Hunters*. Spector, complaining of sudden severe chest pain, collapsed. They moved him to the coronary care unit; someone notified his wife. A nurse on the unit ran to his bedside, a girl he had been seeing. She screamed his name and began to kiss him. She became hysterical, would not leave him, and in that state was discovered by Spector's wife, who had rushed to the hospital. The

40

next day Spector was almost completely recovered. For three more days he was observed; no diagnosis was ever made. His wife and child went back to her parents in Iowa, and Spector, divorced by his wife, married the girl from the intensive care unit.

Padget waited for the doctors to make up their minds about him. His belly was wide open. He was breathing through the tube in his trachea, his respiratory excursion expanding and deflating the black rubber bag. Dr. Patel sat at his head, every fifteen minutes checking blood pressure, pulse, and respiratory rate. She peered over the top of the anesthesia frame. "Have you decided what procedure you're going to do? If you're going under the diaphragm give me a few minutes' notice so I can get him really relaxed."

Dr. Lacey, the attending anesthesiologist, who was also monitoring another case in an adjoining room at the same time, came in about every ten minutes and whispered a question about the condition of the patient to the resident anesthetist. He was the strong, often invisible support to an operation, giving me confidence that the other end is being well managed. Often anesthetists are hostile, maybe because they want to be the surgeon. I had worked with Lacey for years, and his presence in the operating room gave me the security to concentrate completely. It's not good for a surgeon to have to keep asking about the blood pressure and pulse while isolating a cystic artery or identifying a ureter in a mass of adhesions.

I asked my two assistants, "Gentlemen, you know that animals get arthritis, diabetes arteriosclerosis, aneurysms, high blood pressure—tell me, why don't animals get ulcers?"

"I know," Newman said. "According to a new theory by Dr. Schein, it's because they go on all fours."

"That's a little piece of speculation I didn't expect you to pay any attention to. Do you know, Paul?"

"I know you can put a rat in a condition of laboratory restraint and induce an ulcer."

"True. But in its natural state, with all the stresses of evading cats and rat traps, this never happens."

"What's the answer, then?" Newman said.

"A good question. The answer is that nobody knows. History: When were ulcers first described?"

"Who knows?" Newman said.

41

"I know," I said. "How about you, Paul?"

"I'd rather get to Padget's ulcer and do something about it," Spector said. "I don't know if there's any value to medical history."

"It's an intelligent man's obligation to know the roots of his profession." I said. "In the nineteenth century—the century, mind you, of great pathologists like Aschoff and Virchow and Rokitansky—ulcers were very, very rare."

"Now is what I care about," Spector said.

"But you're a surgeon," I said. "And we're treating this ulcer surgically, because Padget's exhausted all alternatives. But in fifty years ulcers may be as defunct as galloping consumption. It's already decreasing in incidence, even among doctors. Surgical treatment didn't start until after World War I, and today in this hospital alone 10 percent of its surgical beds are occupied by ulcer patients."

"I wouldn't want to give up ulcer operations," Spector said. "Now that we can treat it with techniques giving a relatively high success rate and relatively low complication rate."

"Remember," I said, "that's for the group, not for the individual. But it's true we shall someday regretfully say goodbye to this treatment, as the physicians successfully treating syphilis did to malaria when penicillin was introduced."

As I put in lap pads to expose the area where the esophagus enters the stomach I asked Spector another question. I knew what I was going to do. I had always known exactly how Padget's ulcer was going to be handled. But the teaching process had to go on. And teaching is done by asking questions. "So, Paul, what procedure would you do in a case like this?"

Spector answered with the phrase every surgeon uses when he is positive about something. "If this were me, Dr. Schein, I would want this ulcer out and in a bottle. Because it's a bad actor. Two perforations and now an obstruction. It might sound ridiculous and maybe a little horrifying to take out half or more of a man's stomach to eliminate an ulcer the size of a pencil eraser. But it works best."

"Why?" I said. "Why is it best?"

"Because it takes out not only the part of the stomach which has been traumatized but also that portion responsible for producing more acid to make more ulcers."

"Why else is it the best way?" I said.

42

"It's the best way because the ones who write on the subject say it's the best way. You're always saying that you support a point of view by experience. In surgery it's not enough to have an idea or to believe anything; you have to rely on results, what's been published."

"How about people who use statistics more for support than for enlightenment, like a lamppost? What about the risk?"

"You can have a blowout of the suture line. Okay. But how often? Overall 2 percent mortality, 90 percent cure."

"What about the other 8 percent?" Newman asked.

"They have problems, sweating and dizziness after eating—what we call dumping," Spector said. "Or they're excessively bilious and maybe a few have anemia and diarrhea."

"Newman," I said, "since this is your first case and you have no experience, you're spared the knowledge of all the controversy on the subject. You may be divinely inspired. What procedure would you suggest?"

"I leave that to you," Newman said. "But I would worry about the side effects. I read about a lesser procedure with vagotomy. What about that?"

"Newman, in academic circles, when you ask a question you might get a reply, but you also get another question. What's the vagus, and what's it to do with Padget's ulcer?"

I had to go up under the diaphragm and in preparation I lubricated my gloves by wiping them on a moist towel.

Newman said, "It's the tenth nerve coming off the base of the brain. There's a right and a left. It moves the vocal cords, influences the rate the heart beats, has an effect on the in-and-out bellows action of the lungs and . . ."

"There's a student for you," I said to Spector. "Listen to that recital. What else, Newman?"

"Well, about the ulcer. The vagus nerves connect the brain with the acid-producing cells in the stomach. If you cut them, that would be like surgical psychiatry."

"Who showed that for the first time?"

"I don't know any medical history. There's no course in that subject."

"*Dummkopf.* Therefore you're content to be ignorant? So you're going to be another whose interests will be in real estate and boats. There was once a surgeon who wrote a medical history under a pseudonym because he felt his professional reputation would be tarnished by the revelation of an intellectual interest. Apparently medical students—your generation anyway—are equally worried by the history of ideas."

"Come on," Spector said. "What good is all that stuff?"

"Sure," I said. "It's not where it's at, right? You equate an interest in the past with senility. You lack aggressive curiosity, which means you're lazy, and you've surrendered to nonmedical pedants and professional historians who care more for history than medicine. It's precisely in things like the memoirs and collected letters of our predecessors put away in locked shelves in the library that the great truths lie. Well, it takes a Muni doing Pasteur to convince fellows like you he really existed. Okay. Now what about this vagus business, Newman?"

"I know that's the mechanism that made the dogs salivate when Pavlov rang the bell. But that's high school stuff."

"You're right. What year? Nineteen-o-two, right? Then it took more than forty years to apply those observations to a human being. Now, in Mr. Padget here, if we cut those nerves and make a detour in his stomach for the obstruction, we won't have to remove his stomach. That cuts down the risk. But there's some recurrence in a procedure like that—say 10 percent in ten years—and Padget's forty-seven, so he might not like the odds. Spector, would you consider anything less than removing half of the stomach? How about a compromise?"

I handed Newman a retractor—called a hoe—to expose the undersurface of the diaphragm and showed him where to position and hold it. I put a moist pad over the spleen to avoid injuring it, and another retractor to keep it out of the way. Newman was immobilized, a retractor in each hand.

"What we do," I said, "is gamble with experience and statistics. I wouldn't want our patients to know that, but that's the fact. We try to tailor-make a procedure to fit Padget's problem, and we examine the odds—the risks, the complication rates, long- and short-term results. So what about it, Paul?"

"I still think we ought to take it out. But I would accept a vagotomy and removal of one-third of the stomach to get rid of the acid-producing area."

44

"I agree," I said, having made the decision for myself from the beginning. The discussion was to pass the time and maybe to instruct.

Newman bent to look beyond the rib cage. The sleeve of his gown touched my face and I jerked away. "It's okay to look," I said, "but next time ask before you make an unexpected move. Now you're contaminated, and you'll have to change. My face is not sterile. Anything that touches it and is then in the operative field can act to transfer bacteria from my face to the body of the patient. You've broken the chain of asepsis. You'll have to change both gown and gloves."

Had his forearm sleeve touched my gown I, too, would have had to change. It was a nuisance; the operation had to be delayed until he returned and again held the retractors. He backed away from the table, looking embarrassed. "I'm sorry, I just wanted to see up there."

The circulating nurse loosened the tie in the back of his gown and slipped it off from the front by turning it inside out and pulling it over his gloved hands. Then she removed each of his gloves, grasping a fold in the palms, thus avoiding contaminating his hands with hers. Were that to happen Newman would have had to scrub for an additional ten minutes.

The instrument nurse held up a new sterile gown for him. He put on another pair of gloves. No longer made of rubber, principally because of the cost, they are now made of some plastic material. Since nothing could be done in the two minutes it took Newman to change I took the opportunity to impart more information. "Rubber gloves, gentlemen, were introduced by Halsted of Baltimore, not for purposes of sterility but because his operating-room nurse, who subsequently became his wife, thought they were neater and cleaner than working with bare hands. There are still some surgeons doing internal examinations with bare hands because they feel that 'shoes for the hands,' as the Germans put it, impede tactile sensitivity. I have not found this to be the case."

In 1960 I went to Berlin to discuss a surgical procedure with a world-known expert, managing to catch him within a few months of his retirement. After breakfast in his office we went to the operating room for the case he was going to show me. He took off his white coat, I took off my jacket. He hung his tie on a hook, I did the same. He opened his collar and put on a rubber apron and large oversize boots over his shoes. I did the same. We went into the operating room sans cap, mask, and gloves. We both kept on our wristwatches. He operated with admirable dexterity with his bare hands and I assisted. Between cases we changed gowns and rinsed our hands. For me it was an amazing excursion into the past. We then made rounds together. I saw no obvious infected wounds, and when I asked him about his infection rate he looked puzzled and said none that he could remember for that year. So much for Semmelweis.

Newman took the retractors again. I asked Spector to tell the student how we were going to find the nerves.

"They're like tense violin strings. You can almost twang them when you touch them. The right one is behind the esophagus."

I picked it up, a shiny white cord. "Paul, clip it as high and as low as you can go and I'll take out the segment between. Now tell Newman where the left one is."

"In the front wall of the esophagus, and in this you have to be especially careful to avoid making a hole in the gullet. Such holes are hard to close. I saw a patient who had to be fed intravenously for three weeks while it was healing. I don't want that experience again."

He clipped again and I cut.

Newman said, "It looks easy."

"Easy is a word for experience," I said. "It's also easy to cut a blood vessel instead of a nerve and spend a half hour and two bottles of blood trying to rectify the error. Dr. Fisher—you know of my friend, Dr. Fisher?—once blundered in this way three times in one operation. His assistants called it Fisher's anomaly, a good conference term, arterial bleeding from a severed nerve."

6

At the beginning of his second year as a resident, Spector had called for an appointment. The fact that he had arranged it in advance was a characteristic that separated him from the direct thoughtless intrusion of other residents, who, if they had a special problem, would break in unannounced. Spector was a gentleman.

I was at my desk during this lunch period, eating a sandwich. When I wanted to know what was going on in the hospital I ate in the dining room. When I needed, as now, to catch up on some of the journals, I ate at my desk leafing through journals and checking off those articles I wanted to keep which later would be torn out and stapled by my secretary. Time was implacable. The use of my own time had to be subdivided and cherished. I don't apologize for my obsessiveness; I have long learned to live with it. I was willing to give Spector some of this priceless commodity because I liked him, and those attributes of his personality which made him unique were fascinating to me. Like his love for old fountain pens.

He would say, "Most of you fellows don't know that ink comes in bottles, not in those replaceable rods. You don't know what an ink bladder is, you've never wiped off a pen point, or used a blotter. Pens today don't have character, they're used and thrown away. A ballpoint is for filling out a form in triplicate. For writing you need a black Waterman, the lifetime green Parker, the red Schaeffer, and the calligraphic pen points."

He had learned how to repair them himself because pen repairmen were going out of style as their customers vanished. Often, on a chart note, he would use ovals, loops, serifs, and thick ascenders and thin descenders. One of the administrators offered to pay him to do place cards for a board of trustees dinner.

His prize was one pen the size of a magician's cigar which had to be filled with an eyedropper. He called it his camel pen because it had enough ink to last for several weeks. Unfortunately it leaked. It wasn't important to Spector that he change his tie each day, but he never forgot to rotate his pens. Otherwise, as he carefully explained if you cared to ask, they dry out or leak or lose their effectiveness in some other way because they need to be used.

Order was important to Spector. He didn't barge in, and he didn't knock on my door, but went to the secretary, who then told me he was there. He came in wearing his short white coat and blue slacks and shirt with hand-tied bow tie. He looked like a medical student, who would be dressed that way, although the students longed for the full whites of the intern, while the residents couldn't wait for the long white coats of the attending physicians. Spector had been in uniform longer than he cared to be, and he wore just enough to identify himself as a resident. He had made one concession in this first year. He had discarded the paratrooper boots in favor of civilian shoes.

He had a choice of two chairs across from me. One, to the side of the desk, would have meant a friendly chat. He took the chair directly facing me, which, as the psychiatrists insist they know, meant he was interested in a confrontation.

"Well?" I said.

"What I want—what I need to know, Dr. Schein—is how I can learn the technique of surgery. I mean the real minutiae of how to do what and when and how much. How do you learn that?"

"You're kidding," I said. "Would you come in to the Secretary of Defense and ask for an explanation of his budget? What kind of question is that?"

"Look," he said patiently, "suppose you're trying to learn to play the clarinet. Newman tells me each detail is discussed. For example, the fingers. How they're held. What kind of tension. How they should be curved. What part of the key they should touch. How they should be put down and taken off. What alternate fingering is possible, which is the preferable one for making the best connection in a particular sequence. I mean, Dr. Schein, it's all

48

spelled out. I've been a resident for a year and it doesn't seem to me that that approach is used here at all. As a matter of fact, I don't see that anything like that is taught here. So how do I learn?"

"You mean is it the third or the fourth finger that fits into the other blade of the scissors?"

"Something like that, yes. As far as I can tell, everything about the technique is learned from looking over somebody's shoulder, and nothing is spelled out or specifically instructed."

"In a sense you're right. Spector, I'm going to tell you what I did when I was in your position. I'm not suggesting you do the same thing, but it worked for me. Each time I scrubbed with somebody and he did something a little different or interesting I remembered it and wrote it down in a notebook. I wrote sections for clamps, suture materials, choice of instrument, and special techniques. I noticed that, unlike dentists, the surgeon works with one hand. It's not in the books that you be ambidextrous, yet many guys use the other hand in special ways; I noted those instances in which somebody was doing too much, something unnecessary, and as such to be avoided. If you start a male hernia at the top and stay in the thin plane of the hernial sac and everything else comes off, then you know you can't possibly injure the vas deferens, while an insecure surgeon will go looking for it. So part of it is knowing what you don't have to do if what you're doing is correct."

"So how do I learn the technique?" Spector said.

"Take tying knots. We used to practice on bedposts with a cotton spool but that doesn't work because it's not analogous to standing vertically in the O.R. So you ought to practice in a shoe box or a pillowcase. The main thing is clamp, cut, and tie. That's surgery. Take clamps."

"Clamps?"

"The purpose of a clamp is to hold a piece of tissue in a certain position. Every time you use one you injure or destroy that part of the tissue that the clamp grasps. If you take more tissue in than you really need you kill a million cells, and for no purpose, and they can retaliate with excessive pain, poor wound healing, and dead tissue leading to infection. Take the second member of the trinity. Cutting."

"Exactly," Spector said. "How do you hold a knife? Here am I, a

49

resident, I've finished a year in this specialty, and did anybody ever tell me how to hold a knife? Do you hold it as you would a pencil, or as you would in cutting a piece of cake?"

"Tissues have blood vessels. If you make a cut directly across at right angles they don't bleed because the cut end closes off. But if the cut is jagged, made with hesitation, the vessel will bleed. So in an incision a good surgeon may lose twenty drops of blood, a poor one, two ounces."

"I admire the way you're making it clear," Spector said. "So how do I learn?"

"By precept and luck, you wise guy. Take the famous surgeon who was talking about protecting the patient against other surgeons. He said that nobody should be allowed to take out a stomach until he's done a hundred of them. One time that surgeon got sick in the middle of an operation and he walked away from the table and went home. The nurse said to the assistant that he ought to finish up. What, said the assistant, how can I finish up the case without the professor's permission? So deballed were some assistants under some professors. But that was thirty years ago. So look how lucky you are, Spector, being given all this opportunity to learn."

"Jesus," Spector said, "I'm seriously considering going into merchandising."

"And another thing, how does the patient judge the excellence of the operation? By the length and neatness of the scar, right? Yet that's the bone that's thrown to the intern, the final closure; the professor never got around to doing it at all. You'll be all right, Spector, as long as you follow the competent, note the mistakes of the inept, and emulate the masters. Like those surgeons in your hometown, all of whom learned by looking over somebody else's shoulders. That kind of learning hasn't changed at all. Big-city hospital or no. And another thing. We have naturals in surgery just as in baseball. Some guys are born good."

"Since you can't tell me how to learn to be a good surgeon, not in one, two, three steps, anyway, tell me at least how you recognize a good surgeon."

"First, the whole procedure has to look easy. No unexpected happening, because nothing is unanticipated. No hesitation about instrument decisions. No repeated or useless motions. A linear clarity about the whole thing. And if you watch him do another five cases it will be done in exactly the same way, the same number of stitches to close the duodenum. His nurse knows in advance exactly what he's going to ask for, and he doesn't change his mind. He doesn't encounter the surprises that the neophyte does. But mainly there's an aura of confidence; he's been here before and seen all the variations. Rarely does a monkey fall out of a tree, and rarely does a first violinist break a string, but should this happen they recover on three strings or land immediately on all fours. That's a good surgeon."

"He's a combination of monkey and violinist?"

"Now you've got it, Spector."

At the end of each year, in a formal way, I was required to write an evaluation of the residents. I have to answer such questions as How does he get along with the nurses and the patients? How does he get along with his colleagues? What is his fund of medical knowledge? What growth has he shown in the last year? What is his potential as a surgeon in practice, as an academician? Are there any major personality problems?

What I wrote was only partially what I felt about Spector. I gave him high marks as a surgeon, as an individual, but I didn't put down anything about my envy, or my feeling that we were somehow connected.

This although everything I had achieved—my position, my attainment—meant nothing to him. Of life in academia and practice in a hospital setting he had this to say:

"You have this fancy machine that cost sixty thousand dollars, it gives twenty blood chemistry determinations at one time, and I admit it works well for screening—for example, we're picking up cases of hyperparathyroidism which we'd never been able to diagnose before except with advanced kidney or bone disease and we can find it early now and cure them—okay, but when you use the goddamn thing otherwise it can't even tell you if the patient fell out of bed. Like the kids with fever ten days after a ruptured appendix, all you had to do was look at the temperature chart and put your finger in his rectum and feel an abscess—what do you need a machine like that for?

"These hospitals are run by administrators who never see a

patient. Back home we run the hospital—if we don't like an administrator, we kick him out. We're in charge. Medicine has become so complicated at these damn institutions you're at the mercy of the government for grants, or the benevolence of a particular chairman. Even when it works, I hate the system.

"Take the professors. I don't think that to be familiar with all the footnotes is worth all the sacrifices. I'd rather know less and live more. You guys who have to know more and learn more and publish or perish can't possibly have the time for the things I think are important. I doubt, Dr. Schein, you can tell a trout from a mackerel when it's wriggling on a hook. I believe in private practice, and I believe in practice where you know all about your patients. I'm willing to take seeing a patient long after I've operated—somebody I see on the street, say—but you fellows often never see him again. We don't have clinics with patients sitting around all day waiting to see a doctor. At home if they can't afford us, we treat them anyway. I can't stand the dehumanized clinic situation, patients turned into numbers, required to sign the bottom line.

"I think there are simple answers to everything. By the nature of your training you have to see everything as complicated. A conscientious doctor, who's had good training, working in an environment that he controls, can successfully handle the vast majority of surgical problems in a community hospital. The esoteric stuff, or when I find myself in danger of raping your trinity of cut, clamp, and tie, those cases I'll send on to you.

"As for publishing, I haven't written anything since my freshman themes. I know I can't. But I'm going to work in a place where all that doesn't matter. I'm going to be a skilled functioning practitioner and I intend to have a good life. And I promise you, Dr. Schein, if you ever get tired of all this academic malarky you can come out and work with me and make twice as much."

A tempting offer. I saw myself in him. He wanted a one-to-one relationship with patients whom he could make better. I had wanted the same thing, I still want the same thing. A lot of the time I found myself in the center of professorial pretension, still counting the angels on the head of the pin. I might be asked to address a surgical conference on some controversial issue in intestinal surgery; Spector would be addressing the Junior Chamber of Commerce on the history of the fountain pen, having brought in examples from his collection.

52

7

They say I hum while I operate. Mrs. Ellis, the operating-room supervisor, claims she can tell which stage of the operation I have reached by the harmony coming from the table. I am not aware that I make sounds, and no one has ever been able to tell me what portions of which sonatas or quartets I hum. Or maybe they're show tunes or popular songs. The musical subconscious may not be as snobbish as I believe my musical taste to be. When the critical, the delicate stage is reached, I am quiet. This was the point we had reached with Mr. Padget.

An untrained eye looking into his abdominal cavity would see nothing but a mass of unrelated tissue, intestinal coils and the pulsations of blood vessels. Spector and I saw organs, patterns; Newman had seen this before only in cadavers and animals and diagrams.

Surgeons have various ways of expressing tension. Some become hypercritical and abusive to their assistants, others damn the instruments, the stubborn contour of the patient, or the hard-to-manage tissue reaction to disease. There aren't many screamers or instrument hurlers left, although there are cursers whom some old-school nurses refuse to tolerate. There is a story of a famous surgeon who was removing a glandular tumor under local anesthesia. The patient feels no pain, but is fully conscious. The surgeon at one point began to scream at an assistant for help and when the response wasn't fast enough yelled some more. From under the drapes the patient's voice came. "Please, Dr. Intern, do what the professor says, there's a human life here."

Spector said, "Okay, we've severed the vagus nerves, that should take care of Padget's personality problems. Now let's get the ulcer out and give him a new opening for the food to go through."

Up to this moment Newman had been holding the two retractors in midair like a weight lifter. I told him he could let go and he exhaled in relief and flexed his arms well away from the patient. We were now out of the north end of the abdomen and were going slightly south and deep where the stomach and duodenum meet, which was the area of the blockage.

This was the most difficult part of the operation. A one-inch part of the duodenum had to be resected from the surrounding tissues. It had to be cut across, and one end had to be seamed. This seam line had to be tight enough not to leak. Often in this condition the tissues surrounding the ulcers have become so diseased they are like wet blotting paper and will not hold a suture.

An assessment had to be made now as regards whether I could find a zone suitable for proper suturing. If it looked really bad it was possible to back away from the problem by simply bypassing and creating a new opening from the stomach to a different part of the bowel and leave the bad area alone. This usually worked, but it was not as good as cutting out the rotted portion. That decision has to be made while there is a choice, rather than blundering into a problem from which the retreat can be difficult.

I had decided earlier what I was going to do. Sometimes the local situation makes the preoperative decision impossible and you keep an alternative in mind. In this case I decided to go ahead as planned.

The first thing to be done was to control the blood supply to the area. Two arteries, one on the left and one on the right side of the duodenum, have to be ligatured. I carefully separated these vessels from their surrounding tissues by means of very fine clamps, called mosquitoes, and then I clamped and cut and tied. I then mobilized the duodenum gently clear of the pancreas, careful not to bruise either of the structures. I was now ready to cut through the duodenum.

I always return to this area with great respect, as to an old acquaintance whose responses are not always predictable. The tissues respond well to the animal characteristics of a good surgeon—cunning of a fox, a beaver's joy in construction—and the tenderness of a woman also helps.If the tissues are bruised there's a big black eye in the abdomen, and one can injure the pancreas and disrupt enough of it so the digestive enzymes instead of going into

54

the bowel can leak into the peritoneal cavity—and that autodigestion can be lethal.

I didn't want to cut through the pylorus, which is the muscle separating the stomach from the duodenum, so I held it firmly out of the way and cut through the duodenum with a number ten blade. This is a reasonably good-sized knife with a keel blade. What is important is to cut through both walls, each of which has four layers. I put an occluding clamp onto the stomach to prevent leakage and I covered it with a laparotomy pad. What remains to be closed is called the duodenal cuff, because it's like the cuff of a sleeve. A little bile seeps out of the opening. The first suture layer is put on to bring the two walls together, and the second layer covers the first layer and seals it. After that several reinforcing sutures between the capsule of the pancreas and the duodenum serve as the final seal.

I now asked Newman about the importance of the duodenum, and what had he learned about it. His eyes brightened, and I knew he had been studying. "It's the only organ of the body we refer to by its size, Dr. Schein."

"Really? How's that?"

"Because that's what 'duodenum' means. Twelve in Latin. Twelve fingerbreadths long. Each side of the C is four."

"That's very interesting," I said. "Why is it so important, why has it been held in such veneration by the ancients?"

"Well," he said, taking a breath. "There's its strategic location in the body. Whatever goes into the mouth and out of the stomach has to go through here. At least two quarts of bile and pancreatic juices enter it through an opening only one millimeter wide. The two major blood vessels that bring all the blood to and back from the intestines tunnel under it. It's a challenge to the surgeon. Working on it successfully is not for medical students."

"Spector?" I said.

"I believe that one of the explanations for the similarity of symptoms and the interrelation of ulcers, inflammation of the pancreas, and gallstones lies in the fact that they have this common one-millimeter opening into the duodenum. The size of a pencil point. And it's possible that disease in this area can be manifested in any of the three organs, but stemming from the same cause. Something's wrong with the plumbing that the final common outlet should be so narrow. You wouldn't design a sewer system that way."

"God's a poor plumber, Spector?"

"Who am I to criticize? James Joyce died of ulcer disease, you know. It's a bad area for presidents, too. If that same duodenal opening affects the gallbladder then you can also chalk up Eisenhower, Truman, Hoover, and Johnson. Everything the liver makes, everything the gallbladder puts out, everything the pancreas produces except insulin—all of those have to pass through the duodenum."

"And most of the troubles are blamed on the stomach," I said. "Right, Newman?" He had that faraway look that the second assistant gets from being immobilized with the two retractors that they call idiot sticks.

8

I thought I knew where Newman's thought had gone. I remember watching my first abdominal operation, and thinking then of the first days in medical school, wondering if it was worth it, if it had been the wisest choice.

The acceptance letter said that activities for the first-year class would be posted on the bulletin board outside the Student Education Building. This board was the locus for information. In ensuing weeks it would contain lists of group assignment, class activities, lectures, and reading lists. A three-by-five typed card stated that there would be a first-year orientation lecture at 10 A.M. in the auditorium.

Personal notices were delivered to your mailbox in a sealed envelope. These yellow envelopes notified the recipient of a meeting that day with a faculty member. It meant an oral examination, with no time for last-minute preparation. There was no way to escape from it, no foretelling the night before. With the written exams if you missed one you could take it again because you couldn't be penalized for missing a test. So students learned to wait outside the lecture halls until the lecturer went in, thus assuming no exam was to be given during that period. But the administrators spent their time outfoxing the students, and often after fifteen minutes the lecturer would stop, dieners would bar the doors, and exam papers would be handed out. It was a way of medical-school life unknown to the students of today. Yet none of us bled from it. The survivors, that is.

Newman saw Cathy Forge talking to two students in the central hall. She recognized him and waved. He walked over and she introduced him. "I'm glad to see you made it."

She was sunburned, an oversized leather bag with silver buckle on her shoulder, smoking. The other two left and she suggested they go to the lecture together. It was a warm September day. Those wearing vests from which to display their Phi Beta Kappa keys later took them off and never bothered again. In that group these keys were not unique.

The auditorium was so large it went up two stories. There were sidewall plaques commemorating the most generous benefactors. Lesser patrons were identified by brass nameplates on the backs of the seats and the least generous were listed alphabetically on one large plaque between the windows.

The opening speech was delivered by one of the institution's best speakers, a psychiatrist well known to the students and remembered by the alumni for his humility, scholarship, and sincerity. Older graduates said of him that by being one of the humble of the earth he still managed to acquire possession of its best fruits.

"You have already made the decision to be doctors. I think it's the best of choices. I want to welcome you to your first year and tell you something of what to expect. This will be one of your most difficult years. You will have to learn a new language. The names of the body structures will appear to have no logical derivation; you will have to learn them by rote. You will have to develop a new way of thinking, in physiological terms, in the sense that there is a mechanism for understanding symptoms. You will have to sharpen your sensitivity to the emotions of others. We now view the patient as a whole, not as a reservoir of symptoms. When you achieve that much, you will be on your way to joining the profession of medicine. I envy you the pursuits of this year.

"The laboratory faculty has asked that you organize in groups of at least two for the dissections in anatomy and the laboratory experiments in physiology. If you don't have any choices we will arrange it for you alphabetically. Meanwhile, enjoy the excitement of being a medical student."

He nodded, smiled, and walked out.

Cathy said, "Shall we try it together?"

"Sure," Newman said, wondering why she had selected him. She would have been his choice, but he could never have asked. She took out a ringed notebook and wrote down his name and phone number. She wrote down most things. She was bright and

58

organized and there were many things he was going to learn from her.

Oral examinations were given at the end of the first six weeks. In anatomy, instead of the classic approach of dissecting every part of the body, the students reviewed already dissected sections—they would receive a leg, part of a head, a hand—dismembered body parts which came wrapped in formalin-soaked sheets. The arteries were injected with an orange dye. Newman had no reaction; these did not appear to have come from people. Except for the facial parts, whose humanity could not be concealed.

The importance of these orals was that, if passed, there was no need to take written examinations for the rest of the year. Also on the basis of this first quiz, unknown to the students, an evaluation was established.

Newman took no chances. He studied the muscles of the sole of the foot, he learned where on the face the head of a pin would touch five different bones. Before the exam he felt like a glass filled to the brim: if shaken he would spill over. You did not know in advance which section you would be examined in. Newman was assigned to the professor of anatomy who had given the lecture on the anatomy of the chest. He was asked where on the chest do the three lobes of the right lobe come together, how does the blood get from the legs to the lungs, and could he twist a piece of paper to demonstrate the contour of a rib. Newman knew the answers.

Cathy Forge took the exam in the head and neck. He waited for her. She came out smiling. She lived in an apartment away from the school and he rarely saw her after five o'clock; he didn't know how much she had studied. She said, "I just got a new pearl for you. The way to remember the branches and the order in which they come off the carotid artery in the neck. The way to memorize ascending pharygeal, superior thyroid, lingual—all the way to internal maxillary is with this mnemonic—As She Lay Extended Oscar's Penis Slipped In."

In physiology Newman was asked to discuss the function of hemoglobin, the causes of anemia, and the composition of the urine. This was straightforward and simple to him. If he had known it was going to be that simple he need not have studied. Cathy was asked the functions of the liver, the pancreas, and what changes occurred in the blood in carbon-monoxide poisoning. They both decided that there were no trick questions; this was a serious effort to see if you knew the material.

Newman wanted to celebrate having passed. He had no one to celebrate with, and went to a movie alone. He envied Cathy her social graces. She was at ease with the faculty; he avoided them. He believed she was invited to their homes. At the end of the first year Newman was at once exhilarated at having passed, but also miserable because he had no one to help him alleviate his emotional isolation. That summer Cathy was to serve as a volunteer in the cardiac lab in a California hospital and Newman went to the urology ward of the local hospital. Cathy, before leaving, invited him to her parents' home, saying she would be free anytime after the middle of August. In July, not having said anything about accepting her invitation, he got a postcard from her. She had sketched a man in midair over a fence with the caption: Why not?

Newman made his first person-to-person long-distance telephone call the first week in August. She sounded glad to hear from him. Her directions were simple enough; she lived in a small town north of San Francisco; the local train stopped there once a day. Once there he was to ask for the house, a fifteen-minute walk. There were no taxis.

On the way he stopped at Las Vegas. He saw the glitter, went into a casino, and froze with the fear of temptation. And he fled. In San Francisco he visited his former professor of German, the man who had helped him make his decision to study medicine. He was still teaching Goethe and Schiller and Lessing to students who showed little interest. His book on Parsifal was still unpublished. "My boy," he said to Newman, "You made a good decision. You will always be needed. Not like me, lecturing to people who do not care. But here the climate is good."

Newman took the local train. It had five cars, the last one a flatcar carrying lumber. The seats were wooden; it was hot and crowded. It crept along the shoreline. The station looked like a set in a Western movie. The stationmaster pointed out the way to the Forge house.

A pickup truck in the driveway, a summer house with lawn furniture, a grape arbor, and cornstalks. It was sunny and cheerful and quiet. There was no answer to the doorbell chime. He put down his suitcase, walked around the house, and saw no one. He sat outside. In ten minutes an old Dodge came along; an ebullient lady, smiling under her large straw hat, greeted him cheerfully. "Charles Newman, right? Welcome. I understand this is your first visit to California."

Newman admitted it. He helped carry the supermarket bags into the kitchen. It was modern white, an oak table in the center of the room, a restaurant-sized stove, an oversized refrigerator. One wall was all windows.

"Cathy won't be back until tomorrow—sorry about that, she's been called to the hospital. Dr. Forge will be back this evening. I'll show you to your room so you can get out of that collar and tie. We wear sandals mostly; make yourself comfortable and we'll have lunch."

This was all strange to him. He was used to the city heat, the sun reflecting back from cement pavement.

"I thought we'd put you up in Mark's studio. Through the door out there to the right . . ."

Newman walked out into the undisturbed tranquility. The sun produced a pleasant, dry, stimulating heat. He could hear the ocean. He thought it was like being at a seaside Italian monastery. He had never seen an Italian monastery, but he knew what it was like, what it had to be like. That people really lived in a place like this was a shock to his city realism. What you read about was different from the way things actually were, but not here. He thought about D. H. Lawrence in Taos, R. L. Stevenson in the South Pacific, and Byron in Greece.

The studio was a glassed-in afterthought to the main house. A Baldwin piano stood on a small stage. Easel, palette, brushes looked as if they had not been used for a while. He remembered the drawing on Cathy's postcard. A studio bed and rattan chairs. A long table supported on sawhorses and a filing cabinet. A walk-in closet with ski equipment. He hung up his suit and changed into chinos and sneakers.

Cathy returned late Sunday afternoon; one of the staff had given her a door-to-door lift. Above-knee skirt, no hat, smoking as always, white blouse with frank revelation of lack of brassiere. "Hi," to everybody, and to Newman, "You look better already. The rings around your eyes are almost gone and your face looks ironed. I'm beat." She put down her briefcase, took a beer from the refrigerator, and stretched out on a chair.

Newman felt it necessary to talk about what they had in common but he couldn't remember any hospital gossip that was worth repeating. Cathy said she was learning to pass a cardiac catheter but she found it boring.

At supper they had fish in wine sauce, but Newman couldn't tell the difference between the chocolate mousse and chocolate pudding. Afterward he and Cathy went down to the beach and sat with their bare feet in the water.

He said, "I didn't believe this kind of world existed."

"You don't sound happy. You sound defensive and depressed. I just want to ask one thing. You stopped over in Las Vegas. Did you gamble?"

"Well, no."

"You wouldn't take a chance. You know that's your trouble? You know a person could get angry with you for a thing like that?"

"I don't understand that."

"You miss so much. You want to be safe all the time. You could have afforded to lose, even to get hurt."

"Maybe I'll change with the M.D."

"For you it's always the next time."

He looked at her profile and felt stirred up but he didn't know what to do about it. He was silent, but was afraid he was appearing sullen.

"You can't wait, Charlie. Take my father. The first things he looks at in the paper are the obituaries."

"You think something is wrong with me and I wish you would tell me what it is."

"You going to go through life just being a bright student? How can you be sensitive and insensitive at the same time?"

He wanted Cathy to spell it out.

"You do things too fast," she said. "But you don't take the time to savor anything. The way you eat, for example. You force people to hurry to keep up."

"It's my metabolic rate."

"Taste things," she said. "Suppose at Las Vegas you let yourself get excited, suppose you lost twenty dollars. You'd then know something about the gambler's feeling. You have to try things, just to see how you react."

On the tenth day, wanting to stay, he insisted on leaving. Fish and guests, he remembered.

At the station Cathy said, kissing him on the mouth, "I'm still a woman and for me you would have to make the first move. Why didn't you? Born a man, die a doctor?"

9

There is a large clock in the operating room and periodically I look at it. I'm not aware that I do it.

So far in the course of Padget's operation we had cut the vagus nerves, divided the far end of the stomach, which is that part joining the duodenum. Now we had to cut across the upper end so that one-third of it could be removed. We talk of taking out a stomach. What we mean is that we take out part of the stomach. The part remaining continues to function.

I was curious about the time. We had been working forty minutes. This didn't account for the delayed start and the anesthesia time, so it was now nine-thirty. Newman, following my glance at the clock, asked, "How long should it take to do this operation and hook up things together again?"

"That's not an unfair question," I said. "And you deserve a two-plus-two answer. How long, Paul, do you think it takes? You've been involved in over twenty ulcer cases so far."

Spector answered immediately, "It varies."

"There," I said. "Are you satisfied, Newman?"

"I'm serious about this. I don't see why you're making a joke out of it. You start at time X. How many minutes later are you applying the final dressing? Mrs. Ellis ought to know. She has to schedule these one after the other. Is it an hour, ten hours? I understand you don't know much about ulcers, so you can't answer my questions, but surely you ought to be able to tell me about operating time."

"You heard the question," I said to Spector. "Answer the man. It's not a philosophic question, you don't have to be Nathan the Wise arbitrating religions. All he wants is a number."

"Like I said, it varies. The fatter the patient, the more complicated the situation, the experience or lack of it in the surgeon—it varies. If you really want an answer in minutes you have to ask Dr. Lacey. Anesthetists charge by the minute. He can give it to you exactly."

Newman said, "Dr. Schein, give me a number."

With all this cross conversation we never stopped working. I was cutting and tying, Spector was clamping and tying, Newman was holding the retractor. I was preparing to clamp the two large blood vessels at the margins of where the stomach was going to be cut across.

I care about surgery and I care about music and I like to compare the two. This change in pace, this tone in conversation, was like a piano sonata leading in to the second theme. I wanted to prolong the talk as a sort of interposed scherzo.

"I'll answer your question in a minute, Newman. Let me tell you how the old man used to handle such queries. The family of a patient would ask how he was doing and with straight face, he would say, 'If we don't run into complications everything will be fine. If there are complications we'll have cause for concern.' He'd say this with obvious sincerity and the family always seemed to be satisfied."

Spector said, "This kid wants a number."

"If they asked the old man how long a procedure would take he would say from the beginning to the end, he'd never even stop for lunch. But actually, how long? They would persist. And he would use Lincoln's analogy to a man's legs being long enough to reach the ground. If they persisted he would say he had made no other arrangements for his time, or he was not running a train on schedule, and an operation takes as long as it takes. If they still persisted, like Newman here, he had his final answer. He would ask when was the patient's birthday and guarantee that he would be done in time for the patient to blow out the candles. You still want a number, Newman?"

"Dr. Schein, I like your stories, I'll even use them myself without giving you credit, but give me a figure."

"Spector. Give the man a figure."

"It varies. Take any number, multiply it by the variable, and the result is what you're looking for."

"Someday," Newman said, "you'll ask me a question."

65

The time does vary. I was in Greece during the time of the Marshall plan. There was a lot of ulcer disease and no possibility of real treatment with diet and drugs. They took them out because under those conditions it was better than the complications of leaving them in. I saw a surgeon working with two tables in one operating room. Someone else would open and close the abdomen while he went from one to another for the important part. He was experienced, the patients were skinny, the disease rarely advanced. The operation took about an hour.

I told this to Newman. "So that's the number. One hour."

"No," I said. "It varies. We've got one surgeon who takes ten hours. Instead of a clock in his O.R. there's a calendar."

"How long does it take you, Dr. Schein?"

"This guy I'm talking about, when he does a tumor they x-ray before and after because by the time he's finished it's possible the tumor has spread."

"How long, Dr. Schein?"

"It varies. But since you're so compulsive, I'll tell you that the average case takes me between one and a half and two and a half hours."

"How about that?" Spector said. "Dr. Schein gave you a figure. Are you satisfied?"

"Not entirely," Newman said. "Does it make a difference if the same operation takes one hour or ten hours? I'd hate to hold these idiot sticks for that long, regardless of the quality of the peripheral instruction. Meanwhile, do they feed you lunch with a gourmet enema?"

"Newman," I said, "a little after eight this morning you came in here an eager, shy, clean, pure, modest, well-spoken young student. You're in the operating room for one hour and already you've taken on the unenviable characteristics of your garden-variety surgeon. So now you know how long it takes to become a surgical personality. On contact."

"I don't want to develop a surgical personality. I want answers. Does the operating time make a difference?"

"Minor differences in time make no difference—and I won't define minor. Of course, major differences involving increased an-esthesia risks and tissue exposure with consequent infection prob-lems—well, you know about that yourself. You can't control those variables because sometimes the disease varies. But what is not generally known is whether the prolongation is because the disease itself imposed difficulties or the surgeon created difficulties with his own ineptitude. So the time factor alone is no explanation. The fast fellows say the calendar people don't know enough and the slow movers call the others careless. The old man used to say the operation should consume the amount of time necessary to do the job not complicated by blunders, inexperience, and uncertainty."

Spector delivered a silk ligature to me on a long carrier. I laid down a flat, firm knot and put in a second and third one for security. This is the belt-and-suspenders technique which lets me sleep better at night. I once saw a postoperative bleed from one of these arteries and have since always used a third knot. It is still argued whether these sutures should be gut from sheep's intestine, silk from a cocoon, or a synthetic fiber.

The upper right angle of the cut stomach is called the angle of death by the old surgeons because it has to be turned in to prevent leakage. Inappropriate suturing can be lethal.

"You're seeing it done, Newman," I said. "It looks easy. All good work has to look easy. Is it experience alone that counts?"

"What else?" he said.

"Spector?" I said.

"Preparedness," Spector said. "Preparing for each operation the night before."

"How?" I said. "How do you prepare?"

I always ask my assistants what they have looked up about the operation in advance. If the answer is noncommittal, if I believe they have not looked up the material, I limit what I let them do.

"I refer to my commonplace book," Spector said. "The way you told me in the beginning. I look up what I learned not to do, like watching Dr. Fisher, and the trouble he gets into. I amalgamate all the stuff from Harkin's monograph, Maingot's *Gastric Operations,* and the C-Z atlas. But mainly I keep a list of what's best, what has worked without complications."

I keep away from complacency about operating. Each time I hear of a case that went bad that conviction is renewed. I think about the following day's schedule when I'm driving home, in the shower, or in the interval before falling asleep. I consider what might be special about the patient I am going to do in the morning.

I think about alternatives. The process takes a few minutes. About reference books, one must know the authors, the politics that might have gone into authorship and publication, the often limited personal experience of individuals in multiauthored books—I know a surgeon who writes of procedures he has never done. Some texts are like falsies—alluring front and no substance. I go to the books that come from personal experience minutely detailed, with alternatives for the difficult situation. When you're in trouble from an unexpected tear or rip you haven't the time to invent a new technique and it's amazing how stored information is recalled when necessary. For the new entity, the rare case, I will look up the literature several days before, which is the value I get from the tear sheets I continually accumulate; I might call up an associate to get the benefit of a personal experience. As the years go on I am called on more often than I am the seeker.

"Newman, I am ready to cut across the stomach. Is there anything you can tell me about the angle? Wait, this ought to be a question for Spector. Paul?"

"We're taking out about a third of the stomach. So we ought to go from high on the right to low on the left."

"Why?"

"Two reasons. We take out most of the area that stimulates acid production and we keep the *Magenstrasse*."

"Newman, as a student of German literature, what does that word mean?"

"I know the word, not the reference. The street, or road, of the stomach?"

"Right. The road along which the food passes without climbing onto the curb. Who says there's no advantage to a classical education?"

"How come most anatomic terms are Latin and Greek and this one is in German?"

"Mrs. Rodriguez, we're going across the stomach with the staple clamp. Check that all the clips are in place, and that the lockjaw ratchet is turning properly. Last week it got stuck—somebody forgot to fill it."

I asked Dr. Patel if Padget had any problems. "Please pull the stomach tube back so it won't be caught when I clamp."

More than once I've included the tube in the stapling clamp and

68

I didn't want it to happen again. I felt the tube slip through my fingers as she withdrew it into the stomach pouch that was going to remain. "Please fix it securely to his nose, it's going to remain in this position for a few days."

"I'll take care of that, Doctor."

I looked over the screen. Dr. Patel was reading an anesthesia journal. I asked if she were bored.

"Anesthesia, Dr. Schein, is hours of boredom and moments of anxiety. I prefer boredom."

I thought about Billroth.

The first man to do what I was about to do.

Everything I do in the operating room has been done before. It's like a musical score, all written out. Now it's just a question of how well it is performed. But to do this successfully for the first time one had to be a Theodore Billroth. In 1881, without blood, intravenous fluids, or X ray—operating with bare hands and a beard that could have dipped into the wound. A North German come to Vienna as a professor of surgery. Tall, fat, intimate of Brahms, with whom he played piano duets. Successful, but melancholy; for him the glass was always half empty. The first to remove the larynx as well as the stomach, he sent disciples throughout Europe founding what we today have altered into the resident system of instruction.

Before Billroth there were no successful stomach excisions. How could there be? The stomach digested everything put into it. Why not the sutures? He practiced on animals. Twice the operation had been tried by others and both patients died. His Helene Heller survived the operation for a few months, her cancer too far gone.

An innovator, he was still a citizen of his century. He had done what nobody thought could be done. But asked if one would ever be able to operate on the heart he said only an idiot would contemplate such a thing.

"Billroth," I said, "sent his disciples out to teach others to do this operation. It should have occurred to you, Newman, that they spoke German. He worried that some would try it and fail, and the failures would be attributed to the procedure rather than the incompetence of the surgeons."

"Like the man said," Newman said, "to do a stomach you shouldn't try until you've done a hundred."

"I'll tell you about the doctor who said that," I said. "He had an

69

anxious look that his patients thought was compassion. Actually it came from chronic prostatitis and an anal itch."

"So how do you learn to do an operation for the first time?" Newman asked.

"I'll tell you," I said.

The American College of Surgeons was meeting that month and our hospital had been asked to present a wet operative clinic on vagotomy. "Wet" means an actual operation. The operating room would be turned into a stadium, with tiered benches all around. We had never operated on the vagus nerves. Like a neighbor seen and greeted with no relationship established, we had seen them in the path of our scalpels and clamps as we operated on the esophagus and upper end of the stomach primarily for tumors and hernias through the diaphragm. The nerves themselves were never before sought out during our operations for ulcers.

The old man was to do the procedure, and I was to be his first assistant. I was sent to the library for all the available publications and to bring back all the illustrative material. A week before the operation we went to the dissecting room and looked closely at the area in cadavers. We outlined the procedure theoretically, and practiced with the lights and where we would stand and what instruments we would use. We considered all the possible dangers—tears in the liver, injury to the large veins, damage to the spleen, and even a possible inability to locate the nerves themselves. We were like participants in those heist movies where every possible contingency is considered beforehand.

We hoped to have a case to practice on before those we had scheduled for the demonstration clinic, but the usual plethora of ulcers had somehow dried up. The old man called his confreres in other hospitals, but nobody seemed to have any ulcer problems. The night before we had our last dry run, I saw them carrying the benches into the O.R. I couldn't sleep. Suppose we couldn't find the nerves at all—how embarrassing.

I was in early to check the instruments, and rehearsed the details once more with the scrub nurse. The room was filled with visitors. This operation was going to be popular, and all the surgeons wanted to see how it was done.

The old man appeared cool. He talked about physiology, and

the role of the vagotomy in ulcer surgery. The operation went like a dream. Both nerves easily isolated and cut. We passed the segments of nerve around on wet blotting paper.

No one knew that we were doing it for the first time. We were the authorities. They were coming from the small town to see the professors work. One doctor said it looked so easy he wanted to know whether it was always this easy.

The old man truthfully replied, "Each time I have done a vagotomy for duodenal ulcer, it has gone exactly like this."

I said to Newman, "That, Charlie, is how you learn to do new operations."

10

The Von Petz stomach clamp is a combination of a stapling machine, vise-grip, and cabinetmaker's joiner. It opens like a lobster claw. The stomach is grasped between its open jaws. The jaws are then squeezed down. When the ratchet is turned a series of parallel metal clips is pressed out and delivered across the stomach wall. The pressure squeezes the blood vessels and the clips mechanically close them off. This instrument is not used by everybody, I like it because it's clean: there is no spill and little bleeding.

Newman, like all students seeing this instrument perform for the first time, said, "That's a neat trick."

There is a railroad-track look to the series of clips fixed on one side across the two-thirds of the stomach being retained, and the one-third about to be removed. I cut between them and Padget's troublesome section of stomach is in my hand. I give it to Mrs. Rodriguez.

This pale-pink horn-shaped piece of tissue has just finished living. It is a testimonial to medical treatment failure. I don't feel like an executioner although removing a section of stomach is analogous to taking off a finger, a breast, or a leg. The difference is that this piece of stomach and its adjacent ulcer will not be missed. Someday we'll find a better way to take care of this problem than by biblically removing one-third of a stomach to get at the problems caused by a pencil-eraser-sized hole. Someday this operation will fall into the category of taking off a leg because of a compound fracture. Lister solved that problem. There will be more Listers.

In a sense I had now completely severed Padget from his mother's milk and Dr. Jordan's cream.

I had once asked to schedule a gastric "amputation." Mrs. Ellis refused to accept that booking. "We don't do that, "she said; "we do gastric resections or gastrectomies. That other phrase has a bad connotation."

The nurse unsentimentally weighs the specimen. It is 180 grams. She puts it in a wet towel and sends it to the pathologist; one must be sure it's an ulcer and not a tumor. If it should turn out to be a tumor we would have to go back and revise the procedure—which means cutting out more. The omentum and more of the stomach.

"One way to lose weight, Mrs. Rodriguez?" Spector said to the nurse.

He wasn't referring to the 180 grams. With this operation patients rarely regain their original weight, especially women who often lose excessive amounts of weight. In some cases the operation has been done just for that purpose in patients grossly obese. I don't recommend it. There are too many associated problems.

"Stick to your cottage cheese and yogurt, Mrs. Rodriguez," I said. "On you it looks good. Maybe because you're working again. I wish you'd come back to scrubbing instead of teaching. You know what they say. A poor surgeon needs a good scrub nurse and a good surgeon deserves one."

"Physicians, cure yourselves," Mrs. Rodriguez said. "I don't see that any of the three males around this table are markedly underweight. I just want to know if your're going to do a Hofmeister or a Polya."

It was characteristic of Mrs. Rodriguez to be professionally adept. She had come to the hospital as a ward aide on the surgical floor. Her name was then Perez. She stood out because she was eager to help. She assisted with dressings when everyone else was busy. She did things she didn't have to, she knew things she didn't have to know. Temperatures, blood counts, where the trays were, and social details about the patients. She had the good looks of the late teen-ager, but she knew how to smile, flatter, and move. She did not care, or did not know, about women's lib. She saw her sex as an advantage. Men found her pleasant to be around. On her the drab aide's uniform was provocative. A course for O.R. technicians opened up, full salary while learning if you signed up for three years. She went to school during the day, worked at night, and became a superior scrub nurse—calm, quick, and informed.

I sometimes felt she was too serious. I agree that talking at the operating table might spread bacteria but surgical jokes are sometimes necessary to break the tension, not to mention the need for teaching.

We talk at the operating table, and mostly not about the problem. That only comes up when there's somethng unusual or tricky. Mostly, for the experienced, its pretty much the same sort of thing. Almost all the problems have been encountered before. That's what it means to be prepared—it's another word for experience. At this stage in my career it would be unusual to encounter a fish in the milk bottle. The diseased gut can behave in only so many specific and varied ways. One gets to know them. That doesn't detract from the interest in the minutiae, or in my ever-aware need to do it better. But I don't have to verbalize it with a "look, see, and behold." Even technical expertise can get to be routine.

"Back to the European school, Newman," I said. "What's the difference between a Hofmeister and a Polya stomach reconstruction?"

"You don't expect me to know the answer to that," Newman said.

"You could have surprised me. So I'll tell you. It's the way you rejoin the remaining part of the stomach to the intestine. If you use the entire stomach opening remaining it's a Polya. If you close part of it off and make the opening smaller it's called a Hofmeister. And if you can remember that you'll be the only psychiatrist in the world who knows the difference."

"I never said I was going to be a psychiatrist," Newman said. "Although it's true I'm interested in the whole person."

Spector said, "Newman, you're still a kid. You're still in the freshman class. You can't be interested in the whole of every person, that's theoretical garbage. Not only isn't there time, but there are things about a person you shouldn't know. There's personal privacy—you ever hear about that? You can be interested in a person's disease, because you can do something about it, but that's it. Your 'the whole person' is just part of the shrink's bullshit. Why do you have to feel the pain of paying the bill to appreciate the treatment? Just because that was Freud's attitude doesn't mean it has to be true. Although tying in payment with treatment takes care of their collection problems. Whatever rebels there are in psychoanalytic theory, there are no rebels to that practice. Our appendices and gallbladders get better whether the patient pays or not. Those bastards even do it with one-shot consultations; they're the only members of the profession who never give professional courtesy. Why is their hour now forty-five minutes—more precious than the surgeon's, or any other specialty?"

"You're getting too excited, Spector," I said.

"True, but justifiably. I went through this whole business with my first wife. The thing I resent is that a patient will stay with a psychiatrist one year, or two or three or four, and during this time he's closeted with him and the patient doesn't talk about what happens in there and the psychiatrist is ethically silent and who is to judge results? We had two doctors at this hospital who committed suicide while under treatment. That's a mortality rate. We report those things. Does the shrink?"

"You might be viewing only one part of the elephant, Paul," I said.

"I think the whole thing is chemistry," Spector said. "One day they'll find that out. Some defect in the enzymes makes a person act peculiar, we'll give them the enzyme and they'll get better—substitution treatment; faulty metabolism, we'll find something to block the defect. It will all be done with drugs. Give them what they need or remove what they've too much of."

"You think it's that simple?" Newman said.

"The trouble is we're afraid of things being simple. The shrinks pick up on every word, every slip of the tongue. They attach endless and complicated significance to matters that often don't require investigation or explanation. That's why I love Westerns. There are the good guys and the bad guys You have to learn the difference. The white hats and the black hats. Instead of those painful involuted references to Oedipal Conflict and anal and oral arrests. Even Freud said that sometimes a good cigar was just a good cigar."

"You're prejudiced." Newman said.

"Sure," Spector said. "But my prejudice comes from experience. Bitter, and personal. Take George III. Crazy, right? And his insanity affected the founding of the United States. But if somebody had bothered to check the fact that he peed purple and had they the knowledge of analytic chemistry, they would have been able to establish that he suffered from porphyrinuria, and it wasn't because he had psychotic episodes for any other reason. He had a chemical disease!"

"What do you think about all this, Dr. Schein?" Newman said.

What I cared about just then was to close off this angle of the stomach and I wasn't ready to talk. I didn't want to listen either. On the other hand, the mind goes its own way, and what they were saying tied in with what Padget had said to me earlier.

In my office Padget had said, "I'll tell you why animals don't get ulcers, Dr. Schein. They don't play the stock market and see their savings slip through their fingers. They aren't involved in a business where a partner is humiliating you by usurping your position, friends, and old accounts in the name of efficiency and new methods. They also haven't wives who don't understand or don't want to understand what happens out in the jungle, who talk about their self-fulfillment and don't know what to do with themselves on a rainy afternoon. Give those problems to your rats, and they'll get ulcers." He was started now and kept going. "If you have real success and satisfactions you don't get ulcers, you give them. When the Nazis were successful in Poland they didn't get ulcers, they also gave them to the British. When they were no longer supermen in Russia they themselves began to perforate. For me, this whole disease has to do with milk. You don't get enough tit when you're a kid, and you don't get enough of the milk of human kindness when you grow up. Cow's milk is no substitute."

"Are you telling me, Padget, that your sessions with the psychiatrist were all wasted?"

"He explained that my anger and hostility put a hole in my stomach. I understand that. He made me see that my father made me insecure because he built up a big business which I couldn't handle and I had to bring in a partner and problems started with him. Even if that's all true I don't want to know about it. I want to know how to face my wife's indifference. I want to know how to handle my business fears. Neither my wife or the shrink concretely helped. So I went outside my marriage. I got another woman, because my relation with my wife was burning me up; after a couple of weeks a mistress turns into a wife anyway, and I got guilt feelings and came too soon and what was it all for? That's when I perforated the second time. You know how that psychiatrist jerk explained the perforation? He said I was having a digestive orgasm. He correlated my stomach pains with the menstrual cycle of my unresolved sexual ambivalence. I have no ambivalence. I don't like little boys, or little girls, or leather or rubber or train rides. All I want is to be cured. That's why I'm here."

When I went to medical school, of all the professors in all the disciplines to which I was exposed, the professor of psychiatry exercised the greatest influence. The anatomist and chemist were savants, the physiologist appeared to be dreaming of how the kidney tubules produced urine, the pathologist worried mainly about form and pattern. Newman's "whole patient" was seen only in that part of the hospital where the windows were barred and the doors doubly locked. The auditorium in the psychiatric wing was open for demonstration lectures each lunch hour. Lunch hours in medical school could be spent in various ways. One could shoot pool, play cards, go to the library, go out for lunch, or bring lunch to the psychiatric lectures. I took my sandwiches to the auditorium.

These conferences were conducted by a middle-aged, black-mustached, watch-fob-wearing senior psychiatrist who retained the accent of his native Vienna. He was said to have known Freud, to have actually been analyzed by Freud. He was truly a Renaissance man. He quoted in several languages. He drew analogies to anthropology, politics, art, music. He also, which was unusual, expressed opinions. He said what was good and bad. He shared his thoughts. He could mimic, used parody, he hypnotized patients, adding an aspect of theater to the demonstrations. He charmed and stimulated all of us.

It was obvious that I was going to be a psychiatrist.

I remember how he epitomized the alcoholic. He held up a glass. "This is the solution in which alcoholics believe their problems are soluble."

In my final year at medical school I worked in the ambulatory clinic and in the psychiatric ward. That experience caused me to change my mind about medical careers. It was one thing to hear a brilliant exposition of a different case each week; it was quite another to see the same patient day after day. The cases moved too slowly. Too often there was no startling specific treatment, just shock and baths and sedatives. In the ward I met a patient, a young good-looking man who told me he was a diabetic, and a sensitive person, and he was appealing to me because he recognized my own sensitivity, and could I help him, he was miserable in the institution and could I have him released. I checked his chart. This gentle-appearing soul had been found tossing dismembered sections of his roommate's body into the East River, after his friend had told him he was getting married.

Psychiatry, in its pace and lack of the technical manual skills required—although I recognized its verbal skills—lost its appeal. I required something faster, with more certain and ascertainable results, and exposure to a larger group. I get impatient if I have to wait fifteen minutes for a biopsy report.

I understood Padget's disappointment, Spector's skepticism, Newman's search for utopia. I also understood the problems of the psychiatrist. I didn't question the good they do—in those areas where they can take confused, unhappy people and redirect their drives and rechannel their energies. I think their prime achievement is making a patient appreciate pleasure without guilt and to recognize that there are times when circumstances justify unhappiness.

Spector wanted to know how I reacted to the practice of psychiatry. I said that for myself I didn't want to hold up a hand, ask a patient how many fingers, and be answered Red, or January 15, or Cleveland.

11

Newman was one of six third-year medical students who had been assigned to me for a formal weekly surgical conference. There was Cathy Forge; one flat-faced girl with long black hair named Williams; another who was short and fat and amiable, incongruously named Stark; a somewhat foppishly dressed male named Bauer; and one Tucker, who had a handlebar mustache.

There weren't enough small lecture halls or meeting rooms, so they came to my office. Which meant I had to find an extra chair or two and put briefcases under the desk and get the collection of unread journals off to a corner. They walked in looking curiously at the signed photographs on the walls and the books and the revealing clutter. I don't know what they saw, or what it meant to them. But in the seven years I have been receiving these groups not one noted the two cards or ever asked who was the subject of the sketch I have of Beethoven, nor do I think anyone ever knew.

Which is my bias toward the medical students. They come in without preparation for my concept of the physician schooled in the humanities. They can diagnose as "Pickwickian" a patient who is obese and falls asleep from his retention of carbon dioxide, but they don't know the term comes from Dickens. They never heard of Chekhov, and don't know he was a doctor. They don't know John Keats studied medicine and died of tuberculosis. I once asked them to identify the book in which a medical student with a clubfoot has a tragic affair with a prostitute and no one knew. I hesitate to draw literary or historic references because they don't know what I'm talking about. Scientifically, they know more chemistry and physics, certainly more cellular biology and electronics, than I. They really understand the helix, and it gives me trouble. They have an interest in ghetto medicine and medical activism. They are going to be individuals who also practice medicine. But the old notion of total dedication to the profession is one in which I could find few believers.

Now their information and their medical attitudes, for the first time, were going to be directly examined. They had sat through lectures, taken notes, regurgitated them for exams. But nobody until now had pointed a finger, asked a question, and called them by name.

I sat at the desk comfortably unprofessorial in shirt-sleeves and bow tie unslung. A long way from the ermine-trimmed red robes of my medical predecessors. They were in a semicircle before me. I told them what to expect.

My own notion of instruction is, you tell them what you're going to tell them, then you tell it, then you tell them what you just said.

"Your exposure to surgery will be short. For most of you it will be your only experience since most of you won't go on to become surgeons. Most of you will probably not like surgery, or surgeons. Historically we used to rate somewhere behind the medical doctors and the apothecaries. We were the mechanics assigned to the dirty jobs. There are still traces in surgery of our origin from grave robbers, executioners, and military wound dressers. No matter what specialty you pursue there are certain things you will have to learn, hopefully from me, because as doctors it will be assumed that you will know how to diagnose a lump in terms of whether it's important, whether it should be removed or let alone; you will be asked to differentiate between a green-apple bellyache and an abdomen with peritonitis; you will be asked whether this is an infection and should it be opened or given antibiotics. If we teach you this, our minimum purpose will have been accomplished.

"We will make an effort to teach you far more. In that context each of you will be asked to present a case in detail. You may choose any case you like. You will present it completely with all the X rays and laboratory detail, and you will present it without notes. I assume you will have looked up some of the particulars around which the case pivots. I will supplement your discussion. When your case will have been presented each of you should be left with a good knowledge of that particular disorder."

Tucker, with the handlebar mustache, said, "I understand you've already assigned the first case to Cathy. What kind of cases will we be expected to present?"

"Choose the most common ailments. Leave the esoterica alone, at least for the present. Try to cover the things we really see. Gallbladder disease, breast tumors, ulcers, peritonitis, cancer, blood-vessel problems. Bear in mind that the most common diseases occur most frequently." I liked that, and waited for a reaction, and didn't get it.

"Dr. Forge, I'm ready for your case."

This is the time we begin calling them doctors. The title isn't earned yet, and in some cases the use of it is derisive, but they are going to be white-coated and walking around the wards, and I want them to be able to reach upward.

I had noticed Cathy Forge in the hospital. Most of the male doctors had. The average female medical student tends to be round-shouldered and sloppy and understandably tired and worried-looking. Cathy was always immaculate, clear-eyed, hair shining. She was never overtly provocative, and she looked like what we hoped our daughters would be. She had an odd voice—deep alto with a throaty resonance and a barely perceptible vibrato. One turned to look where it came from.

Cathy Forge started with labeling the patient, something we usually have to teach. After fifty abscesses, tumors, fractures, in room thirty or seventeen or eight—which is how the cases are referred to and always forgotten—I want some characteristic of the person mentioned in addition to his disease.

"This red-headed lady who is related to the counter man in the luncheonette across the street"—she didn't say patient or woman —"has a twenty-five-year history of indigestion and has been intermittently treated for duodenal ulcer. It has never bled, never perforated, nor caused obstruction. The ulcer shows up on repeated X-ray examinations."

"That's straightforward enough," I said. "Is there anything in addition to her past history or physical examination that's important?"

"She's disabled only a few days a year with indigestion. I can't feel anything in her abdomen."

81

"Then let me ask you," I said, "why are you presenting this kind of case? It seems much too straightforward for professorial discussion."

"Dr. Schein, we usually get to present complicated surgical problems, and most of the technical discussion is over our heads. This is the kind of patient that those of us who aren't going to be surgeons will probably meet. She's unhappy with her ulcer, she suffers heartburn and belching, and in discussing this among ourselves we don't know what should be done with her."

"What do you mean specifically, what should be done with her?"

"Well, should we recommend a psychiatrist, does she go to a medical man for antispasmodics and antacids, do we recommend surgery, or a trip to Arizona? Or a pat on the back, and you're going to be okay?"

"Dr. Newman. What do you know about ulcers in women that's special?"

"They're less common than in men."

"Okay. What else?"

"Women appear to be more resistant to certain types of ulcer-producing stress."

"Really? Where did you get that?"

"Statistics. During the last war, perforations in men went up threefold; in women there were no changes."

"Listen," Bauer said, excited with information. "Isn't it true that for a time they were giving female hormones like estrogen to men with ulcers, just for that reason?"

"They tried that, but we have no real evaluation of whether it was any good. Dr. Williams, do you know anything else about ulcer disease in women? Any addenda?"

"No, I don't."

"That's better than guessing and being wrong. This way you get a zero, otherwise it's minus two. Let me ask you, Williams, would you have this patient psychoanalyzed?"

She tried to look thoughtful. "It wouldn't do any harm."

"Is that a declarative statement? Would it do any good? Would it be worth the trouble?"

She answered with what was going to be her standard reply: "I don't know."

82

I decided that grading Williams was going to be a problem.

"Let me tell you something about women and ulcers. There are some interesting facts you ought to know. The daughter of Charles I of England, who was Henrietta, the Duchess of Orleans, had a long history of dyspepsia and she died suddenly in 1670. Her father, the king, was suspicious that she might have been poisoned by her husband. The king had an autopsy performed. She had a perforated ulcer. One of the first proven cases."

"Carlyle," Cathy Forge said.

"What about him?

"His rats began to gnaw at his stomach from the time he was twenty-three. And continued through his *History of the French Revolution.*"

"And he lived to be—?"

"Eighty-six."

"And his wife, Jane?"

"One of history's biggest shrews."

"You know, Dr. Forge," I said, "you've reached me. You may even pass this course."

"What about the role of the psychiatrist in this kind of case?" Newman said.

"I will consider it only for those patients who volunteer the information that they're unhappy and have problems. It has to come from them. These chronic gastrointestinal diseases are difficult to treat, even psychiatrically, and if the patient doesn't know he has a problem he may be better off."

Newman said, a little hesitantly, "Isn't that the characteristic antipsychiatric surgical approach?"

"Of course," I said.

Because I sometimes get fascinated by stupidity I asked Williams, because she looked half asleep and hadn't been able to answer anything yet, giving her a chance to evaluate a problem based on common sense, "Would you have an X ray taken every year of this lady's stomach?"

"Yes."

"Why?"

"To see what's happening."

"What could happen on the X ray that would make a difference?"

"I don't know."

"So why x-ray?"

She shrugged.

"Williams, let me explain something to you. A patient who has a duodenal ulcer has a lot of acid in the stomach. Such stomachs rarely get cancer. Therefore, for that purpose we don't need an X ray. The treatment will depend on whether or not the patient has symptoms. We treat the symptoms, not the X ray. If he has symptoms we treat the patient regardless of the X ray. If the X ray shows an ulcer and there are no symptoms we don't treat the patient. This applies only to duodenal ulcers, you understand. Gastric ulcers are a completely different entity."

Bauer, pencils sticking out of his red vest, said, "Apparently, Dr. Schein, you wouldn't send this woman to a shrink, you don't think it necessary that she be x-rayed—"

"Once a duodenal ulcer, always a duodenal ulcer," I said.

"It never goes away?"

"If it does, the potential for recurrence is always there."

"And if she isn't sick enough to warrant surgery, what then do you do with her?"

"I'll tell you, Bauer. She needs the licorice treatment, or some variation thereof. You know what that is?"

"No."

"I know it's not in the book. Not yet. But our grandmothers knew about it. Licorice contains carbonoxlone, which appears to protect the lining of the duodenum. Meanwhile, I would treat this lady with the usual no aspirin, no smoking, no drinking, and a bland diet as a concession to custom, which is probably better than to try to answer why the diet is not scientifically sound. Any other questions?"

Stark asked, "Dr. Schein, since this is a surgical clerkship, will we do any operating ourselves?"

This was on the mind of every student coming onto the service. They want to sew up wounds, do spinal taps, they dream of taking out an appendix or doing a hernia—somehow they always hear of some mythical student who had been allowed to do that.

Was it possible they were naïve enough to believe we would deliver trusting patients into their inexperienced hands?

Yet between the two World Wars in Europe some surgical

careers were started by buying cases from internationally recognized surgeons. For a stipulated sum he would allow them to do cases under his supervision, and one would buy a certain number of stomachs, cataracts, tonsils, prostates, etc. Some of our busiest surgeons got started this way.

"You will get some direct operative experience. Assisting. Which is a euphemism for holding retractors. Yet I promise that those of you who are hungry for the experience of taking a scalpel to the body will get the chance to open and close the abdomen, take out the appendix, gallbladder, spleen, and portions of the intestines. And you will also remove a lung. You're smiling. I promise you, you will have that opportunity—in the dog lab."

12

When Spector finally achieved the status of chief resident, after four years of training, the most important aspect of his new position, from his viewpoint, was that now, for the first time, he was going to get the important cases, the opportunity to do major intestinal and vascular surgery. He would also be directing the diagnostic studies, the preoperative preparations, and the management of postoperative complications. This was the art of medicine within the practice of surgery.

Up to now he had been sent for the X rays, getting blood counts, starting I.V.s. The surgery was restricted to minor amputations, varicose veins, appendices, hernias, an occasional gallbladder when it was thought he deserved it. A rare intestinal anastomosis for dead bowel, but that always during the hours when his superior in rank preferred sleep. He had only a few of these but he sucked each such experience dry. These few cases had made him reasonably proficient in putting ends and sides of intestine together. He remembered his hometown criteria for effective joining: watertight now, and forevermore. Hundreds of dressings of other surgeon's incisions; he had observed that when you didn't know what to do with something you bandaged it.

He started the final year eagerly, only to discover that along with his new opportunities went new responsibilities. While he was permitted to do the surgical work he had been panting for, he was now also the administrator. He was responsible not only for himself, but for those beneath him. Nobody blamed the lowest man in the table of organization for his derelictions, but the man ultimately responsible, and that was Spector.

"This administrative crap is eating up my energy," he complained to me. "Why should I lose sleep over the fact that an immature house officer insulted a nurse and she is demanding an apology? Why do I have to suffer because some kid failed to order no breakfast for a preop patient? The doctor should have told the patient not to eat, the surgical intern should have written N.P.O. and didn't, and the nurse shouldn't have let the dietitian bring the tray, with a no-breakfast sign posted at the door. Neither of these characters did what they should have, so now the operation can't be done, and who's responsible? Me."

In self-defense, and remembering his background, he instituted a semimilitary regime. He insisted that rounds began at a quarter to seven in the morning; he let no one leave until evening rounds were accomplished, and each patient was discussed with the chief. He himself remained in the hospital several nights a week. Despite the new rigors of his administration the younger men liked him because he let them do the ever-increasing violence-induced cases of the changing neighborhood around the hospital. He didn't expect to do many gunshot wounds and stabbings back home in his private practice anyway.

Despite his troubles with the attendings who blamed him for the derelictions of his staff, he was still fortunate in coming to the hospital after the days of the surgical emperors. When I did what Spector was doing they were still in flower.

The old man who was otherwise a gentleman could become a maniac in wrinkled green. We were doing a pancreas resection. It was not only technically demanding but it was one of those days. Everything went wrong. We didn't have all the required instruments; we did have an inexperienced nurse. Everything we touched bled, tore, or moved out of position. The old man grew more and more irritable. To retain self-control he had the habit of leaving the table and washing his gloves in the stand-up basin. Now he had worn himself out just from going back and forth.

He began to scream. "Hold this, hold that, help me here." That was followed by "Anticipate! Don't get ahead of me! Stay in touch! I can only tell you, only God can give you understanding."

Nature was no help. Those exasperating little bleeders that usually stop by themselves turned into torrents. The old man turned venomous. "Why the hell—don't you see—don't just stand there—"

I was reaching the point where I was considering giving up surgery, especially giving up surgery with the old man. I was about to tell him what he could do not only with this operation but with this residency when he turned and walked out.

More senior surgeons walk out of operating rooms with the cases unfinished than might be imagined. I remember one man who encountered massive bleeding which could not be controlled by anything except pressure. Time in an operating room has its own logic. Forty seconds often can be sworn to have been five minutes. This gentleman said to the resident assisting him, "You take a pad and hold it firmly in place. I'm going down to have lunch." And he did. When he came back the bleeding had stopped. Patient pressure in the area will often do the job that suturing can't.

Left alone with the other assistant, we finished the pancreas case, working slowly and carefully and not yelling at each other. I went back to my room and lay down, and considered whether surgery had been a correct choice, whether having to go through this kind of humiliation was worth it. The phone rang and one of the floor nurses said the old man was waiting for me to make rounds. I told her to tell the old bastard she couldn't find me. A few minutes later he came slowly into my room. He sat in the only chair, looked me in the eye, and said, "You know, Schein, you must have left your sense of humor behind. What we both need is to get out of here for a couple of hours."

We went downtown for steaks and beer and talked of what we would do with a similar case next time. I felt close to him. It was hard to recognize the O.R. tyrant in the now solicitous chief.

I discussed this dichotomy with another resident, who told me of his experience. We had once been involved in a particularly bloody business and the old man had his head down and was intent on the bleeders and was yelling for help but the only way he knew to ask for help was with vituperation. The assistant, himself thoroughly disgusted with the progress of the case, yelled back, "Go to hell!" The old man, without looking up, said, "Never mind apologizing, just help me."

He once invited me to his home for dinner. We had a fine meal, and I noted the rewards of a successful private practice. His two daughters, still young, were already being made aware of the social advantages of meeting young doctors. In the three hours I was away all hell broke loose at the hospital. Someone had ruptured the sutures in his abdominal wall and nobody knew where to find me. When I was finally located and rushed back to the hospital the old man screamed at me for not leaving a number when out of the hospital. I had foolishly thought that a social evening with the boss precluded that kind of continuous availability.

Spector classified the surgeons with whom he worked according to what he was learning. He particularly liked the ones who made errors, so that he would know what to avoid. In that field Fisher was his favorite. Fisher once was holding a piece of intestine, felt a lump, decided it was a tumor, cut, and found out it was his finger. Spector sewed him up.

One was a virtuoso on the skin but was always amazed that the abdomen contained the guts. Another operated like a surgical primitive: he had absolutely no sense of perspective. One was timid, running from disease. One had huge insensitive mitts for hands. Another could have rewritten Gray's *Anatomy,* discovering things never before seen. He was an expert in double-tonguing —one for the things seen at the operating site, and the other for the same events discussed in conference.

He had to adjust to the idiosyncrasies of his mentors. Spector was mature enough not to get entangled in the web of trivia that is seen in professional strains, questionable indications, and lines of referral. These were outside his control.

His back continued to bother him. Because he was taller than his attendings, he had to stoop over the O.R. table. He couldn't very well ask the Napoleons to stand on a raised platform. He would have been told to dig himself a hole. For his aching back there was the comfort that in a few months he would determine the height of the table.

Spector's hands lost their early clumsiness without becoming facile. Technical talent manifests itself very early. We had an orderly in the hospital who was allowed to do some lacerations. He was a man without education who had been watching for years. He sewed with tenderness and amazing dexterity. He didn't know what triangulations, undercutting, tension release meant—yet he was able to do it. A plastic surgeon, himself injured, once came in and asked that that orderly work on him.

Spector had once considered veterinary medicine. He found out that torsions in horses—twists of the intestine which impair blood supply—were then not attempted to be cured by surgery. A horse in such trouble was killed, and the diagnosis confirmed by autopsy. It was then that he went into human surgery, where it was considered worthwhile to cure a condition like that. Spector's attitude was that there was no case he should not be allowed to do—under supervision. "My quid pro quo," he said, "a return for years of scutwork." He considered it his right to choose the people he worked with. He wanted to see the tricks, the little details that are the art and make the difference. With some surgeons he learned how to avoid complications. With Fisher he learned what not to do. Starting a procedure with Fisher, Spector would jestingly intone —"Now let us pray."

Spector also learned one final aspect of surgical conference-manship, how by acquiescing in silence to confirm the statement made at a conference by a surgeon explaining the complications of a case not always confirmed by actual events. You didn't alienate your teachers; you attributed it to willful or faulty recollection. He was there to learn everything he could; he was not there to reform.

Padget's operation was going smoothly, which was the time not to feel complacent. We still had to close that dangerous angle of the stomach at the upper right side. I whipped in a series of locked sutures over the clips for security. I prefer to turn in the end with a purse-string suture.

"You know what that is, Newman?" I asked.

"What it says, right? When coins were kept in a leather pouch with a circular string around the neck which, when pulled taut, kept the contents from spilling out."

"Excellent," I said.

I put in a wide purse-string suture and tucked in the corner of the stomach deep in the middle of the circle so that when tied it would be buried and could not leak. I'll sleep easy tonight.

13

Some of the older hospitals still have large open wards with twenty to forty beds. With the advent of insurance plans, which brought privacy within the grasp of the average patient, hospital rooms are now two-, four- and six-bedded. There are advantages and disadvantages to this. The old way was easier to manage for mealtimes, it was more convivial for some kinds of patients, but in any case this has now, in the United States, become a pattern of the past.

Padget was in a room with two beds. We came in for rounds and drew a right-angled curtain around his bed. He looked up in some apprehension and some curiosity as I came in followed by Spector, an assistant resident, and the six medical students. This was the teaching round, as distinguished from the rapid work rounds in which complications are assessed, dressings are changed, and orders are written. The patient, who has been waiting anxiously for a word with his doctor, gets his complaint out as soon as the resident appears in the doorway. It's either Doctor, I haven't been sleeping, or Doctor, I haven't had a bowel movement, both symptoms the resident is least interested in. He's interested in the fever, or the redness around the wound, or why the leg is swollen.

There's another special type of rounds. Those aimed at impressing a distinguished visitor. Scheduled far in advance, it's possible to concentrate the most interesting—a euphemism for the unusual that works out successfully—cases in one area. It's O.K. to walk by a few minor mishaps, but the major blunders—by nature or by man—are, for that hour, mysteriously whisked off for an X ray, to rehabilitation, or just to elsewhere. It avoids the need to explain and keeps the published image untarnished while preserving the truth that minor complications are, even here, all too human. The experienced have so developed the art of roundsmanship with regard to mishaps that they rival the pentecostal repentant sinner whose detailed descriptions of her lapses keeps the audience curious and sympathetic.

"Mr. Padget, these doctors will be participating in your operation and your aftercare, and we're here to discuss your case."

Some patients derive benefit from the feeling that there are a number of doctors involved in their problems and are flattered that they are interesting to them. I didn't know about Padget. He looked a little morose and a little suspicious.

"You're teaching them, right, Dr. Schein?"

"Well, that's part of it, yes."

"I don't know if I want to be an example. I'm sick, you're my doctor, what do I have to do with all these people?"

"The answer to that is simple. Every one of these minds can help. One might pick up something that everybody else missed. You think there's just you and me, Mr. Padget? There's a team here, a large and competent team, and everbody contributes something, and it's all for your benefit. Stop complaining, you're lucky."

"Well," he said, "go ahead. They going to examine me?"

"No, we're just going to talk about you."

He was an exception to the touch-and-smell experience that makes rounds important to the students. We could have discussed his case outside, or in a seminar in my office, but that way would have been a textbook exercise, and this way it was a person reacting.

Spector said. "This forty-seven-year-old man has had two perforations of a duodenal ulcer, treated each time by closure. He now presents with gastric outlet obstruction. He is scheduled for operation tomorrow."

Williams, the girl whom I was trying desperately not to characterize as the stupid one, said suddenly, "Mr Padget, are you constipated?"

"Sure," he said.

"Are you sensitive to that, Williams," I said, "because a woman is regarded as a constipated biped with a backache?"

"That's sexist," Cathy Forge said. "I really think that's unwarranted, Dr. Schein."

92

"I was just quoting," I said, reacting mildly. "Referring, of course, to female patients in a hospital setting. Williams, do you think constipation is a disease, a symptom, or an attitude? Should we take it seriously, or discount it as of little consequence?"

She gave her best answer in six weeks, a flicker of sense. "It varies." Then she killed it with "Doesn't it?" And so her brief light went out.

"In my hometown," Spector said, "it's still no stool, no school. And right after breakfast, or it doesn't count."

The surgeon tends to treat this condition, if functional, with barely solicitous nonchalance. First, because it's not happening to him, and mainly because it's the problem of some other specialty. There are times when it could be a serious manifestation of disease, but this wasn't true of Padget. I considered, and rejected, a number of stories. Like the patient who was ninety-two and complaining of constipation but who rejected a cathartic because he didn't want to become addicted. In this city two daily bowel movements are required for good health—one for the inner and one for the outer woman. Yet constipation is an ancient complaint. In the age of the mummies, there were Egyptian doctors who routinely purged noble ladies three times a month.

Bedside teaching was introduced by a man named Boerhaave in the early eighteenth century. Before that cases were presented in an amphitheater to hundreds of students, and seeing close up, touching, and smelling was impossible. In addition to being a teaching situation there's also the dramatic, because surgery as a profession appeals to frustrated hams. Reputations are founded and maintained and worked at on ward rounds. Bon mots are cultivated in advance, and flashes of insight often come from prestudy rather than spontaneous intuition. Roundsmanship is played by a new interpretation of the obvious, picking up something previously unnoticed, or by a request for data on a test known not to have been done.

Doctors would like to be right. Failing that, they would like not to be wrong. The pros and cons of any single diagnosis are based on one's own personal experience plus what one has heard and read. There is no point in communicating an uncertainty to the patient because we don't want him to speculate about therapeutic approaches. The patient makes two decisions. One, he selects you as his doctor, and two, he agrees to let you operate. You don't really want his opinion about the choices you might have to make. He doesn't have the basis for an opinion, only the feeling of what he'd like which is based on ignorance, hearsay, or gut reaction.

It's easy to lead rounds. One must be brilliant, original, perceptive, and aware of esoteric references. Everybody likes the game. You could see the residents getting ready for some Aunt Minnie story, a diagnosis made not by reasoning out from symptoms, but because you recognize Aunt Minnie from having seen her before.

Bauer, the student who was sure he was going into surgery said, "Because this man has had two perforated ulcers, is it necessarily certain that his obstruction is due to scarring in that ulcer? Isn't it possible that the obstruction is due to the adhesions that might come from any operation?"

"Possible," I said, "but unlikely because that would be rare in this area, and X ray identified the more common cause." And the development of the other condition by Aunt Minnie reasoning is much more consistent. "I'll give you a pearl for making the correct diagnosis. Remember it. I tell it often because it makes a good point. If it quacks, has webbed feet, and walks on land with a waddle and swims by paddling its feet, then it's more likely to be a duck than a chipmunk. Also, take the case of the professor with the trained fly."

"What professor, what trained fly?" said Spector, who had heard the story and was willing to be straight man.

"This professor had a fly which he had trained to jump on command," I said. "He demonstrated before a group of fellow professors. He placed the fly on the table, and yelled, 'Jump!' The fly obliged. He pulled off one wing and yelled, 'Jump!' The fly obliged. He took off the other wing and yelled, 'Jump!' The fly didn't move. 'Thus proving,' said the professor, 'that when you take both wings off a fly it becomes deaf.' "

"Hey," Padget said. "That's not a bad story. But I hope you're not that kind of professor, Dr. Schein."

I smiled, thinking may be I was that kind of professor. Maybe we all were. We hang on to a truth until somebody comes along to disprove it, and that happens all the time. We never used to put ice on burns because it felt too good so maybe it was the wrong treatment. We used to believe gargling was good for tonsillitis, and taking out tonsils was good for people. We used to keep people in bed for weeks to prevent hernias after surgery, and now we get them on their feet immediately. So all we can do is know what's best for today.

Stark, the fat student, said, "How many units of acid does this man have in his stomach?"

"Who knows?" Spector said. "We never determined that."

"Since this is a disease supposedly produced by acids, wouldn't that be important to know?"

"Well, it would not make any difference since what we're treating is the effect of the acid, the blockage."

Tucker, touching his drooping mustache, said, "I think Judy is making an important point. We keep hearing that acid is responsible for ulcers and you don't know what his acid is? It seems to me a vital piece of information is lacking. Or is this determination only done experimentally on animals or on TV commercials to sell antacid tablets?"

"I'll give you a clinical answer," I said. "We think acid causes ulcers but we don't measure the acid to diagnose the ulcer. We rarely do that, unless we suspect a particular kind of ulcer. Are we sure that acid causes ulcers? No, we're not. Maybe it's the enzyme pepsin. Maybe it's something we haven't discovered yet. This whole area is empiric and pragmatic. We do something because in most cases it works. Tomorrow we might be curing ulcers with antienzyme pills. Today we do what works today.

"If we put the same amount of acid into a cat that a human being has in his ulcer, that cat does not get an ulcer. However, if we take all of the liquid stomach contents of an active ulcer patient and put that in a cat it will not only get an ulcer but that ulcer will perforate, sometimes in under two hours. Q.E.D.—something besides acid produces the ulcer."

"Maybe," Padget said, "you should have this conversation out in the hall. I don't know if I feel better learning that you don't know why you're doing what you do."

"Because it works," I said.

Then I did something that usually I would not do without knowing a patient well. I took a chance on Padget. I said, "Is there anything you want to ask, Mr. Padget, with all this talent around to provide the answer?About your operation tomorrow, that is. We give out no stock-market information here."

"Yes," he said. "How long am I going to have to have that tube in my nose after the operation?"

"Padget hates N.G. tubes," I said. "Spector, you've passed hundreds of these tubes. Answer the man."

"We'll leave it in as long as necessary," he said. "Not a minute longer, not two seconds less."

Sooner, I thought, if the operation is done well, with little of the bruising that swells and closes the opening. In Europe they use the tube when indicated, here we do it prophylactically. Because here we have more operations done by inexperienced hands.

Padget could talk in such terms because we had discussed this before. He knew we didn't know. When it becomes necessary to obfuscate the facts in a patient's hearing, we have recourse to medical abbreviations, jargon, and surgical lingua franca. In this instance I could have used D.U. meaning duodenal ulcer, H.C.L. for acid, N.G.T. for nasogastric tube, subtotal for removing part of the stomach.

"Dr. Forge," I said, "what are the disadvantages to using the nasogastric tube?"

"It can produce sinusitis, damage the gullet, and sometimes create problems in the suture line."

"How do you know that? Why don't you apply for a surgical residence?"

I didn't know how, as a third-year medical student, she had the information a second-year resident was just beginning to find out. Common sense and corridor conversation could account for only some of it. I was curious.

14

Following rounds I would normally have gone back to my office for the solitude I required, rationalizing the time by going through my mail, looking at some of the surgical journals, maybe filling out forms. Now—and it had to do with the stimulation coming from Cathy Forge—I didn't want to be alone. I wanted to see people, I wanted to hear hospital gossip, I wanted a few moments to be, in the therapeutic sense, impersonal.

Some of the best places were gone. There used to be what was known as the "tea hour" in the library. Miss Booth—tall, thin, virginal, glasses-wearing New Englander—made a pot of tea (donations were assessed) from loose tea; there were no cookies served; you washed your own cup. Attendance was privileged. You tasted the tea, complimented the librarian on the blend, found people you wanted to talk with. That's gone now. Miss Booth retired. She had no successor. Now there's an open staff T.G.I.F. session on that one special day of the week, which is noisy, too relaxed, with none of the peaceful charm of Miss Booth's daily interlocutory.

The second choice, now also gone, was Sam's barbershop. The place was septic—you cringed when after dropping a comb on the floor he picked it up without wiping it—but Sam's tonsorial skills were secondary to his privileged information. He cut the hair of the great, and knew in advance of any of the staff what was forthcoming in promotions, advances, staff changes, contemplated and actual. On the wall Sam had pictures of doctors and administrators, past and present, glowering down in donnish admonition that this was no ordinary barbershop but a favored place, a sanctum for a confidant. Sam was proprietary, you felt the care of your hair more his province than your own. Passing him in the hall, if you had been so disloyal as to have had your hair cut by someone else, he recognized the alien scissors and chided you. "Dr. Schein, for the director I'm good enough, but not for you?" Sam had power. He shaved and haircutted the patients and with a smirk, a gesture, could indicate they had made the wrong choice of doctor, or, if he liked you, could elevate your importance. But mainly, he knew everything, who was getting a divorce, whose contract was not going to be renewed. I'd have gone down to him now for an unneeded trim, but Sam died of a carcinoma, being as mortal as we all are, despite his hospital association.

The new barber doesn't know anything about hospital politics, but his shop has other virtues. He's an arrested violinist, and maintains his classical associations by keeping a radio going tuned to WQXR. He also keeps a collection of girlie magazines. As you wait your turn you are both soothed aurally and stimulated visually and it's possible to forget you are a professor waiting for a haircut. It is sometimes necessary to be just a man waiting for a haircut.

The only place left was the coffee shop. It has almost no virtues. It's crowded. It's basically for anxious relatives of patients. You don't want to sit there because they might be relatives of your patients, and it's a bad place to discuss cases. The coffee is usually terrible and, worse, is served in paper cups, made more easily handled, but no tastier, by the plastic cup holders. The food is almost as monotonous as the food in the hospital cafeteria.

Well, there wasn't any other place to go, so I went there. And saw Cathy Forge sitting alone, a cup of coffee in front of her, sitting tranquilly without the need to bolster her solitariness with newspaper or book, just sitting and having a cup of coffee, occasionally glancing around at the people. That was her quality, her ability to be self-contained, not embarrassed by herself. She intrigued me.

Cathy appeared to have that gift for living that some have for playing the piano. When I was a freshman in college I attended chapel regularly because it was compulsory. Attendance was taken. Men of different religious denominations alternated in speechmaking. I remember a Jesuit. He came out onto the proscenium—the chapel hall was also used for theatrical presentations, or maybe was always used for that purpose—and with his toes almost curled onto the edge of the stage he spoke about Jesus, the Carpenter of Nazareth, and the veneration of human craftsmanship. That in all achievement there is the need for recognizing that one is intrinsically alone, and that this is the reason for acquiring an education, since, being alone, one should guarantee being in good company. I recalled that Goethe spoke of his writings as the children of his isolation.

Cathy, in her self, in her nature, by a native good fortune, had anticipated and seemed to possess all the skills so endlessly postulated by spokesmen for religion and psychiatry, in all the self-help books.

Goethe, in *Trilogie der Leidenschaft,* at the age of seventy-three was made aware that a young lady in whom he was interested was not interested in him; and for the first time age, rather than inclinations which are undimmed by one's years, asserted itself as the unconquerable enemy. I thought about this as I moved to take the seat next to Cathy Forge. I was not as old as Goethe was then—I was less than twice Cathy's age—but I was now aware of the problem as I had never been before, because I was suddenly for the first time recognizing that my interest in this girl went beyond my view of her as a bright and promising student. Having recognized the interest, my mind went leaping into the possibilities. Analyzing it as a surgeon, the risks went far beyond the possible advantages. If rejected I'd be depressed and embarrassed. If I didn't try it I would be denying myself the variety of experience in the Jamesian sense, since contact with another human being, regardless of her age, given the manifest advantages of Cathy's personality, had to be beneficial. On the other hand, there was the risk of exposure, always possible in the closed environment of the hospital.

In plain terms, could I afford it?

I looked for evidence to cool my interest. She was now wearing glasses. I realized that her eyes had always needed help, but up to now she had relied on contact lenses, through some temporary irritation now discarded. The cool blueness of her eyes was diminished. Today there was a hint of the sloppy in the way she was dressed, she was rumpled from a day at work, the top button of her blouse was unbuttoned, and instead of being deliberate incitation it was simply carelessness. She was seated, but I suspected that the careful alignment of hose would not be there, the stocking over the Achilles tendon possibly wrinkled.

I was protected. I sat down and said hello.

She acted pleased to see me. Remembering my last experience with the coffee, I ordered hot chocolate. I would have ordered cake, but Cathy's abstemiousness was an implied rebuke. I have a great fondness for chocolate cake. I had always thought one couldn't really ruin chocolate cake. Whoever bakes for the hospital coffee shop had managed it. A piece sat facing me in the plastic enclosure on the counter and I stared and conquered temptation. Even if it wasn't quite as bad as I remembered, what would Cathy think of one so undisciplined?

She said, "What about Padget's tattoo?"

I said, "What?"

"Padget. He has a tattoo."

"What do you know about tattoos?"

Cathy shrugged.

"Then I'll tell you. Commonly you'd expect it as part of circus personnel—dwarfs, wrestlers, jugglers, knife throwers, fat ladies, sailors, acrobats. Actually it has a venerable history. It's found on the skins of Egyptian mummies, two thousand years before Christ. It became a fine art in Japan as early as 600 B.C. Many of the South American and North American Indians were tattooed. For a while in the British Army deserters were labeled with a D for deserter, or BC for bad character. It was a fad for a while among prominent people in England, including members of the royal household. Now it's been used among addicts to conceal needle-injection sites. Most people have it done before their twenty-first birthday, impulsively. The proverbial sailor goes through the process of getting stewed, screwed, and tattooed. What else can I tell you?"

Cathy's eyes were shining. Now I knew why she was informed far beyond her years and medical status. People gave her information, and she was a sponge. Young residents talked to her about cases. She was an active listener. She was aware of her sex, and also used it to attract extracurricular conversation. I had also wanted to talk to her.

What was important was that she had noticed Padget's tattoo.

100

She had gone beyond the site of his surgical problem to view the whole man.

"What do you think the significance is?" I said.

"It's part of his medical picture, isn't it? Ulcers. Migraine. Unexplained diarrhea. The tattoo during some emotional problem."

"Psychiatrists never undress patients," I said.

"What a great point," Cathy said.

"Why a butterfly?" I said. "And why on the slap area of the shoulder?"

"Fascinating," Cathy said. Some people use the term to slough off unnecessary detail. To Cathy it was truly fascinating.

I warmed to this girl. Protectively I looked for some more negative areas but I couldn't find any.

"You're really an unusual professor," Cathy said.

"How is that?" I said modestly.

"Why surgery?" she said.

"Two Socrateses are too many for one conversation."

"You're just not the surgical type."

"What type is that?"

"Oh, you know, bluff, truck-driverish, basically unfeeling. I know a lot about you."

She really was an unusual girl. I liked her in glasses.

"What do you know? And how do you know it?"

"Rumors pass around about any faculty member. I know that you're interested in art and music. I know that you take two evenings a week to play the clarinet with a chamber group. So why surgery?"

"What else?"

"Psychiatry, maybe. Or medicine."

"Let's examine this business about the personality of surgeons," I said. "True, many of them, no matter how brilliant at cocktail parties, might not necessarily qualify as people you want as friends. If psychiatrists are doctors who hate blood, surgeons might be doctors who are not interested in people. To get into the blood and guts certainly requires a dispassionate approach to personality. On the other hand there can be a dichotomy so that one clamps, cuts, and ties with his hands and is compassionate in his spirit. I am

101

known to be brief with patients. I walk in, say, 'You look fine, Mrs. Blank, you're going home on Thursday,' and walk out. Once I had a lady stand with her back to the door and say she wasn't going to let me leave unless I could give her five minutes to answer her questions."

"Did you?"

"What choice did I have?"

"But you do care," Cathy said.

I thought I was now in deep water. There were things I had never said to anyone on casual acquaintance before. Cathy locked her eyes in mine. She wanted me to talk.

"When I was young at this," I said, "what I wanted was to work brilliantly at my trade. If it was a bad lung I took it out and if the cancer had spread I took out the pericardium and the ribs and the diaphragm and finally the determination of what went into the bottle and what went back to the bed was which part still had the heartbeat. So I was convinced I had performed some exceptional work, but after a while I realized that all that radical stuff didn't result in much salvage. So I drifted into the area I'm in now, the abdomen, and what I do now results in more cures, and that's what I care about."

"Not always."

"No. And when I have not been able to help I get depressed about it. Physically sick, not an expression."

"So the surgeon can feel."

"Why not? Why should one not be able to do what is needed with his hands and still have capacity for an emotional response? Not always, but often."

"Why not always?"

"Because I react to people for what they are, or what I think they are. Just the having of a disease, in a depersonalized sort of way, doesn't call forth a gut reaction. I require some sort of defense against the inequities of who gets sick. Some poor souls can't elicit anything more than polite detachment. The clergy is reputed to have greater ministerial capacities than the doctors. Maybe that's the difference."

There was a pause, while everything I had said went into Cathy to be sifted and become part of her. Then she said, "But you haven't answered the question."

"What question?"

"Why surgery? Why, even, medicine?"

I had already been disarmed and exposed too much of myself. I was vulnerable. There was a sandwich eater at my elbow, a plate of soup before the diner at Cathy's. The counterman, with beard and no mustache, stood before us with pad and pencil balanced, wanting two coffee drinkers to make room for the more serious eaters.

"Another time, Cathy," I said.

15

I looked over the anesthesia screen at Padget's face. The endotrachael tube, well taped to prevent slippage, was in his throat. Every ten minutes the anesthesiologist-resident recorded blood pressure and pulse rate, and with the same pencil underlined key sentences in a medical journal she was reading.

Dr. Patel looked up at me. "Everything all right, Dr. Schein?"

"Yes. How is it on your end?"

"Routine. Is he relaxed enough for you?"

"Yes. Fine."

I wondered, and forgot to do anything about it later, whether any studies had been made about the dreams patients had under anesthesia. Whether they dreamed at all. I had never had the experience myself. Should I have had? Should surgeons undergo surgery the way psychoanalysts have to undergo psychoanalysis for their own qualifications?

An hour had passed since I had first talked to Patel. During an operation my concentration is away from the north end of the table. I assume that all there is going well. So when there is no problem an anesthetist is a necessary nonperson. When things do not go well I am aware of activity instead of silence at the other end, or the blood gets dark, or suddenly there is no bleeding when there should be, or the patient begins to jerk or hiccup. Otherwise I follow the advice of Dr. Lacey, the attending anesthesiologist, which is to leave that part of the procedure to him and his resident. "You do the plumbing and I'll manage the poisons," was the way he expressed it.

Part of Padget's stomach had been removed and delivered to the pathologist. Through the intercom had come his voice verifying that on examination the section of tissue formerly living inside Sol

Padget was truly part of his stomach, the specimen showing a healed duodenal ulcer. Since the ulcer was in the specimen I knew I had included a cuff of duodenum; I asked about malignancy and he said there was none.

I was about to start the anastomosis. In Greek this means to furnish with a mouth. The part of stomach already had one—temporarily clipped closed, and now I had to make another one in the loop of jejunum, which is the second third of the small intestine, and the two had to be joined together so whatever Padget ate could now find its way naturally into the bowel. There were fifty years of medical controversy about the best method of doing this, and it had still not been resolved. I have solved the problem for myself, because the way I do it works. Too often beautiful hypotheses about the best way to do this sort of anastomosis are destroyed by the ugly fact that they don't work satisfactorily.

"This is the part I want to see," Spector said.

"I'll give it to you, Paul," I said. "The result of twenty-five years of experience. Pay attention, because this method cannot be learned from a book alone, and it can't be bought, and there's no reason to reinvent it after it's been around for twenty-five years."

"I want to see this too." Newman said. "I've learned enough by now to know that this part has to be done perfectly if the patient is going to remain symptom-free."

I looked at him over my face mask and he said hurriedly, "I don't mean that any part of the operation should be done carelessly. I'm talking about this kind of anastomosis, the way it has to be joined."

"Not too long," I said, "and not too short a loop. Plumbing, and gravity. About eighteen inches along the jejunum is where the opening ought to be. If the opening is too far along the stuff can accumulate and be regurgitated. You can't convince a patient who vomits to be happy about losing his ulcer. And if the loop is too short you can get increased pressure, which can blow out a suture line. Which accounts for the rare fatality in this operation. Next, should it be over or under the colon, or should we push it through the mesentery? I do it in front of the colon. Why? Because it works better that way."

Newman said, "But isn't it true, in all deference, that there are surgeons who make shorter loops and do it behind the colon?"

"Yes. And they get good results. But I learned to do it this way from the old man, who did it this way, so there you have two generations of experience. It's true you might find two generations of experience doing it the other way. I have no quarrel with that. In this business what counts is the end result. Still there are people who use statistics like the blind man with the lamppost—more for support than for illumination. I know a man who has been doing it his way for twenty-five years, and his only postoperative deaths have been from heart attacks. On the other hand his patients are religious and view dying as God's will, not surgical error. And sometimes he operates at night."

"What's that got to do with—" Newman was confused, which was a state I occasionally liked to foster in him.

"A surgeon is a day person. Choose your operating time, if you are a patient with the power to determine those things, close to eight in the morning. Surgeons get tired, just like everybody else. Of course they have more energy than most people, so their fatigue is not always as noticeable. Where are we?"

As I talked my hands were busy. "I am going to make an anastomosis two fingerbreadths wide."

"I saw someone do it a handbreadth," Spector said.

Newman said, "Here's your chance to make the opening bigger than it was. Like giving a man a two-car garage instead of the old one-car garage. Why not?"

"Take cosmetic work," I said. "The purpose there is to restore the norm. In ablative surgery in the bowel our greatest hope of restoring natural function is to recapitulate the normal. This is the size opening into which the stomach was designed to open. Why improve on nature? You can restore a nose to be a fine-smelling apparatus but you also want it to look like a nose. If it looks like a nose the chances are it will function better as a nose."

"I wish," Newman said, sounding plaintive, "that there weren't choices in surgery. I wish there was one right way and you learned it."

"In music," I said, "you might shorten one note, but then you have to lengthen the next to make the beat come out properly. Here your choices have to be circumscribed by duplicatable experience. When you are too inexperienced to make judgments of your own you accept what you see done and do likewise. You don't have to

106

operate the rest of your life the way Schein does. But you take from Schein and maybe later from other surgeons and after a while you operate like Newman. Bearing in mind that Newman, as Schein, does not originate, he adapts."

"What gets me," Newman said, "is that you're so positive. Aren't you ever unsure?"

"No," I said.

Which, largely, was the truth. I could have left it at that, but Newman was my student, and not only did he need to know more but I needed to say it. How else was I to be aware of where I was, and what I had learned, and what was worth passing on?

"Cut, clamp, and tie," I said. "That's what surgery is. Maybe that's all that surgery is. Preceding it, of course, is the diagnosis. If it's correct, you go in and find what you expect to find, and you do what you have been trained to do, and you get out. But sometimes the diagnosis is wrong. Again, having been trained, you do what there is to do. You either have to remove something, or sew up a hole in either blood vessel or bowel, or you have to reroute something. It's all nothing but variations on that same theme. And the variety is not only not infinite, but is predictable, and even in disorder there is order."

"That's a swell statement," Newman said, "but I don't know what it means."

"What I say, Newman, refers to the abdomen, because that's basically the area I've staked out for myself. When I was a young surgeon, and arrogant, I said my province was the skin and its contents. So one day I'd put a pin in a hip and the next do a thyroid and then bypass an obstructed artery in a leg. If something extraordinary occurred then I wasn't always as confident as I am now. I open an abdomen and see what I have always seen, the structure there of man. I know how it's supposed to work and I've seen virtually everything that needed my intervention—virtually everything. I can still get surprised. But even within the surprise I recognize the laws of disease manifestations and despite nationality and religion and economic status there is nature's cause and my effect." I stopped to admire that last.

"Are experience and skill enough?" Newman said.

"What are you looking for, metaphysics? Well, often something happens that I can't really explain. Sometimes I need a particular bit of information, or knowledge, and when needed it comes. Something I read in a journal, something I discussed with a colleague, and when I need it, it pops up from unremembered sources."

"Given all that, what makes one surgeon superior to another?"

"First, there is the obsessive personality that insists each procedure has to be done perfectly. There is the ability to recognize that among the many alternatives there is one that is the best, viewed as the gambler views the odds. He comes to the blackjack table with an index. He counts the high cards and the low. He knows the number that are out. From this he has memorized the percentage probabilities for drawing a low or high card. This is when the game is honest. Nature doesn't always play fair. That's the variable."

"I wonder what Dr. Fisher would say about all that?" Spector said.

"He would say," I said, "that's a lot of crap."

16

"What we're going to talk about today," I said to the group of students, "is the diagnosis and treatment of the perforated gut. The abdominal emergency. Have you all copies of Zachary Cope's *The Early Diagnosis of the Acute Abdomen?* Or have you at least read it?"

Bauer, the mustached young man who was definitely going into surgery, nodded. Cathy Forge smiled. Newman looked doubtful. Stark, the short round girl who was going to be a pediatrician, pulled the slim maroon-colored book from her shopping bag and waved it at me.

Vesalius and Harvey and Claude Bernard are behind glass-covered shelves. Cope shares what used to be a monopoly of knowledge. He filtered the facts into simplicity. For the doctor learning and confronted with a practical problem Cope has the answers. Stark had been on emergency-room duty; having Cope at hand made a difference in the management of patients. I gave her an A in my mind. Williams, with the flat face and dull eyes and carefully combed hair, had never heard of him.

How do you deal with a seminary student who knows nothing about the Bible?

Some books are more quoted than read. Cope's was to be digested, as part of the basic training not only of surgeons but of doctors in all specialties. He had distilled what was known and fashioned an invaluable handbook that sits with the stethoscope in the side pocket of the student's white jacket. One of my reasons for visiting London had been to see the Wellcome Medical Library. On Euston Road, the library is a scholar's delight, warm and commodious and helpful. To their staff, after a while, my repeated visits made it apparent that I was there because of interest in the books and not merely to see the collection of apothecary jars. One of the librarians, shirt contrastingly collared, immaculate and yet with a hint of dishevelment to show he was a bookman, said yes, he had known Cope, the old gentleman used to come in every day to read there.

It had never occurred to me that he might still be living. If I could meet him, it would be a little like talking to one of the prophets. He lived, the librarian said, in Oxford with his daughter and her family. Yes, he had the address.

I took the eight-o'clock train to Oxford. There the stationmaster had never heard of the street, and had never heard of Cope, but at least I was in Oxford and could spend my time profitably looking at the colleges. Still, before giving up hope of finding Cope, I went outside to talk to one of the taxi drivers, because they have to know more about street addresses than anyone else. And the driver said he knew of a street that sounded like the one I was after, but it was spelled differently and did I want to be taken there? I said I did, and found myself deposited outside a small house at eleven o'clock in the morning of a Saturday, and I began to feel a little helpless and a little like a pushy American and I wasn't sure I wanted to pursue this. But if I left now I would be forever uncertain, so I rang the doorbell.

A child opened the door and I asked if Sir Zachary Cope lived there and the boy said that was his grandfather and would I please come in. His father came downstairs and ushered me to a small parlor, and Cope's daughter came in and brought tea and cookies. I thought how this access was rare in my own country, where a strange visitor would be viewed with suspicion, with documents of identification required before the door was opened past the chain. Her father, Sir Zachary, the woman said, was now nearly ninety, somewhat hard of hearing, but otherwise hale and would be glad to see me. Then Cope came down the stairs and I rose to greet him, feeling a little nervous, and the great man said, "Dr. Schein? I know your book *Acute Cholecystitis.*" For me, we had both been knighted.

I had expected a tall, imposing, overbearing man. Cope was short, gracious, and humble. He told me how his book had come to be written. Returning from duty as a doctor in the Middle East

110

during the First World War, he became an admitting officer at a hospital in London. There he saw cases of advanced surgical disease in which the diagnosis could have been made by physical examination at a less advanced stage. In talking to some of his referring colleagues, it was apparent that their minimal bedside instruction had failed to emphasize early diagnosis by physical signs, a deficiency due to the amphitheater method of instruction then prevalent. His book, for which there was then and now a tremendous usefulness, reduced diagnosis to the simplest common denominator. Factual, direct, and capable of being understood by any student.

"He makes clear," I said to the students, "how you tell the difference between a surgical abdomen and green-apple colic. If you get no other referral from me, you will have learned about an invaluable vade mecum in Cope's book. So how can you not have a copy?"

I looked at Williams. She was looking as if in some far-off dream of becoming a movie star. I said to her, "Now that we've gotten away from treating intestinal injuries with oil of turpentine, tell me, now that the surgeon had advanced from his status of bath attendant, barber, wound dresser, wigmaker, and executioner, what happened to a man who sustained a gut perforation during the Revolutionary War?"

She looked vague, which was normal. I waited. She said, "I don't know much about that period."

"Bauer?" I said.

"He died."

"How about the Civil War?" I said to Williams. "What happened to a man with that kind of injury?"

"I was a chemistry major," Williams said.

I looked at Bauer. "He died," he said.

"And in the First World War?"

"Me?" Bauer said.

"Your associate is kind of weak on wars. I'll get back to you in a minute, Williams. I don't want to pick on your not having a history minor."

"At least half of them died in World War I," Bauer said.

"And in World War II, also," I said. "At least 25 percent with severe abdominal wounds died. Today?" I waited for a volunteer.

111

Cathy said, "If you could get him to a major surgical facility in time, and if he didn't bleed out immediately, we could probably save him."

"Let's talk of a hole in the bowel." I said. "Let's stay with that for a moment. Williams, why did he die, up to World War II? Why was that poor soldier in trouble?"

"Soldiers—?" she said.

"Anyone with a hole in the gut," I said. "Civilian, knife or gunshot, or tumor or ulcer. Why couldn't they be saved? Or, first, what's the generic term for hole-in-the-gut and its complications?"

"I don't know what you are getting at, Dr. Schein."

"Peritonitis," Stark said. "I read that in Cope."

"Excellent," I said. "Williams, the gut is in the peritoneal cavity, right? And infection there is peritonitis. Okay? Now why did patients die then?"

"No transfusions?" she said.

Williams always made my blood pressure rise. She was not good for my coronaries. But I couldn't ignore her. She was a basic problem, and I had to do something about it.

"Maybe transfusions would have helped," I said, trying to be kind. "What else didn't they do for the patient?"

"Antibiotics?"

"In 1776? We're talking about a hole in the belly, Williams. What didn't they do, because they didn't know how to do it?"

She was blank, as usual.

I looked at the others, each of whom had the answer but because they were now sophisticated medical students would not blurt it out. I had to give Williams one more opportunity. I said, with a patience I did not feel, "Look. Williams. We have a hole. Untreated, it results in spreading peritonitis, and the patient invariably dies. Now what didn't they do to the hole?"

She shook her head.

"What didn't they do, because they didn't know how to do it?"

She didn't say anything.

What did I want of this poor stupid student? I wanted her to be able to tell me that the thing to be done was to close the hole. To sew it up. And surgeons couldn't do that, not until about a hundred years ago, when the philosophical doctrine was dispelled that you

112

couldn't put sutures into the intestine because it would be digested by the same mechanism that digested the food. When the philosophers left the laboratory to the experimenters then the problems began to be solved.

For blessed intellectual relief I asked Cathy, "Forge, why does a patient die of peritonitis?"

"There's a combination of reasons. First, the bacteria produce infection. The loss of fluids from the bowel and the infection disturbs the normal balance between the cells and the blood and the tissues and when this balance is irreversibly altered cells die, and if enough cells die so does the patient."

"What's the surgical management of all this?" I asked Williams.

"I don't understand what you're getting at, Dr. Schein."

"It's the hole, isn't it? What do you do with that hole?"

Somebody whispered fiercely, "You close it."

"And treat the infection, and correct the imbalance of fluids," I said. "Do you see that now, Williams?"

"Ha, ha," she said.

"Williams, how would you make a diagnosis that a man has perforated some part of his intestine?"

"Take an X ray."

"Williams," I said, slapping myself on the temple, "you've just annihilated thirty centuries of diagnosis, of asking the patient where it hurts, how it began, and at least two thousand years of examining the abdomen for signs of peritonitis. You make the diagnosis, Williams, by talking to the patient and feeling the abdomen. The patient tells you where it hurts, and you palpate for tenderness, rigidity, and rebound sensitivity. The X ray is either ancillary or superfluous."

On my desk is a sheet with each student's name and picture, with space for my written evaluation with columns headed Superior, Average, Poor, and Fail. Horizontal columns ask for my opinion in the areas of Fund of Knowledge, Applicability of Knowledge to the Clinical Situation, Interpersonal Relations of the Students to Their Colleagues and Patients, and finally their Potential As a Doctor. Just above where I am to sign my name is space for a final grade: Superior, Pass, or Fail.

Forge was obviously Superior, Newman above Average, Bauer

and Stark were solid Average. But what was I to do with Williams?

Once accepted in medical school, the washout today is virtually unknown. It was not always so. If you couldn't pass the written examinations, and the oral interview confirmed this was lack of information and not paralysis of function, you were asked to resign or repeat the year. If you appeared hopeless even these alternatives were not open to you. In medical school the same criteria used to apply as in other fields—in art if you couldn't paint and you had no sense of perspective or color you were advised to seek another field. In music if you obviously were neither a performer nor a composer you were told you were wasting your time. In medicine this rarely happens; we find all sorts of excuses for intellectual poverty. The faculty is reluctant to bell the cat. No one wants to take the first step. There is almost a sense of guilt in the judge who is required to point out the intellectual deficiency if the student is unable to master hundreds of facts.

There are those who are born musicians or painters; there are no born doctors. The facts have to be painfully acquired. The talent in science lies in the ease with which these apparently isolated facts are acquired, the duration of retention, and the applicability of that information in all its permutations and combinations.

Williams was a dud. I had to say so. I had to fail her. One whose medical career should be at least reevaluated. But why by me, and why so late? She had at this time almost completed medical school. Her quiet incompetence had evidently been disregarded.

Although I would give her a failing grade in surgery, it would not surprise me still to see her in the halls for the next year and a half, and I would tacitly accept seeing her name on the graduation program the following June. And when I pass her in the corridors it will be I who feel guilty.

In medical school the admissions committee accepted her on the basis of personality, potential, and past performance. I would fail her on the basis of lack of information. I found her unfit to graduate. But she undoubtedly would.

Williams lacked the aggressiveness and cunning of an incompetent medical student I knew who slipped through the system and became an incompetent house doctor, in which position he sold transfusions, accepted tips for beds near the window, and for a fee

114

arranged for a special specialist's consultation. As an intern he had already built up so large a patient following that on coming into the emergency room they asked for him personally. When he went into practice he was honored by the community. At a time when few of us could afford a car, he was already driving a Cadillac.

Williams, at least, had humility. So I hoped she might be aware of her own deficiencies, and end up in a practice where she might be free of challenge, willing to refer all doubtful cases to competent colleagues.

At the end of the session Cathy Forge, I hoped by intent, lingered to collect her books and papers and the two of us walked out together back to the hospital. It was a brisk day and I never get enough exercise, so I stopped at the entrance to suggest a walk around the block.

"Sure," she said.

We walked without speaking for a while, our shoulders occasionally touching, and I considered again what every professor reaches the point of considering, at one time or another, when he has a bright and appealing female student. It was pleasant to contemplate, but I was not too anxious for specific progress.

"Are you enjoying it?" I said.

"The day? Our walk?"

"The seminar. The subject. The teacher."

"You're a chameleon," she said. "First you break the pattern of the cold unfeeling surgeon, I find you interesting as a man, a humanist. Then you revert, you become hard, you turn mean."

"I? Mean?"

"Well, you were pretty rough on·Williams."

"All I did was ask her the same questions the rest of you are supposed to know the answers to."

"You really kept pushing her."

I couldn't ask a student her opinion of another student. Nor could I discuss one student with another at all. But I could be general.

"Do you think being a doctor is a high calling, Forge?"

"Yes."

"And the profession has always insisted on peer review, we weed out our own incompetents, right?"

"I suppose so.

"Wrong. What we do about them is nothing. If anything, we even encourage them to slide through and when they go into practice we are responsible if eventually a patient is maltreated, or diagnoses are missed, or incorrect. And if you're not a student to start with, at an age when study comes easily, how do you continue in a profession in which there is never an end to the knowledge required?

"Every ten years there's a large turnover of information. It's the old aphorism that it's not only what we don't know, but what we know that ain't so. And these idiots almost always are complacent about their ignorance. They come blessed with pride and avarice. So if I believe I can stop one along the way I do it."

Cathy made a sound of unhappiness with her tongue against her upper teeth. "I know there are bad doctors—"

"I'll tell you about a fellow I knew, one of the worst residents we ever had. He went into practice and one day he said to me with the twisted vainglory of his kind, 'Schein, I took out thirteen appendices today.'

"So I said, 'Really, Tom? Any of them diseased?' He never spoke to me after that, but you know what? The profession never got to him. Eventually it was the I.R.S. that brought him down."

"I'm not in favor of the uninformed disinterested student or incompetent doctor," Cathy said. "But some students might just be overwhelmed by certain professors. They couldn't come up with the right answers even if they knew them because you've tied their tongues."

"You think it could be that? In a way I hope that might be the reason. But it isn't. Anyway, my grade is not going to stop her. Because my grade isn't going to be noticed by anybody. It will have no effect. Dumb as she is, she's going to sail right along."

"If I were you, and I really believed that—"

"Yes?"

"I don't know what I'd do. I'd certainly want to do a lot more to change the way things work."

"Maybe you will," I said. "Maybe people like you will."

And I felt sad because people like me certainly weren't going to be activists. I was complaining the other day about the infirmity of

116

one of our county medical organizations, and had it pointed out to me that I hadn't been to a meeting in seven years. So much for men of good will.

We had come back again to the hospital entrance. Cathy said, "You never answered me from the other day. You were going to tell me why you elected surgery."

"I owe you that answer," I said.

17

Having determined which two segments of Padget's bowel were to be connected, all that remained was the mechanics of doing it. If you sever a garden hose and then link it together so that the result would be as good a passageway as before it was cut, that's what an anastomosis accomplishes. We were to fit the retained portion of the stomach to the jejunum, part of the small intestine. And to hold each section firmly in place to make it ready for suturing one has to place a holding clamp across each end.

We used to clamp with devices so heavy and rough that the surface had to be shod with rubber sleeves in order not to injure the tissues. In surgery, one moves from the gross to the fine. Cut, clamp and tie. Now the clamps are finer, and infinitely varied in form. We used to cut only with knives; now there are dozens of scissors with different shapes and curves and angles. Now, to hold the bowel, I asked for a curved intestinal clamp on a long shaft. Instead of the originally conceived straight line, the curve gives more access at the edges, and it can be fitted more easily under the rib cage. The two clamps would be finally held by Newman, and I wanted him out of the way, hence the long shafts. In its evolution we have lost the name of the man who first devised this, and the longevity of his instrument has probably outlived every other facet of his life. Immortality in surgery is achieved when an instrument or surgical procedure is identified by name. To become an eponym is to have made it beyond the tombstone.

We develop instruments all the time. Completely new ones, of course, are rare, but we can always bastardize and demand new variations. I have devices made which utilize the handle of one, the shaft of another, the gripping edges of a third, broken up and

118

reassembled as I find an instrument maker that can understand what I'm talking about. I operated on a man who was a tool and die maker. Afterward in discussing the fee, I said I would accept whatever his insurance would pay, which is often far from the fee a surgeon demands, if in addition the man were to make me an instrument. I needed a retractor for fat people. The patient made me an instrument that was double the usual width with two wings having a dam effect to keep intruding coils of bowel from creeping into the working area. This instrument is manipulated into the abdomen the same way a baby is manipulated out of the pelvis, rotated and tilted to take advantage of the widest diameters. I call the retractor a Pickwick. Few nurses and colleagues know why. Dickens and I know.

Certain procedures are often done less than perfectly because there is no instrument adequate for the situation. A case in point is in the manipulation of an inflamed gallbladder. It's like a squirming wet infant that has to be held in position before anything salutary can be done to it. Too often the clamp we had to use would perforate the organ or slip off.

I was once in London and had lunch with a famous surgeon. I was then just starting and I held that great surgeon in veneration, his having agreed to meet and talk to me a signal favor. Here was a man whose textbook of operative technique I had read in several editions. I do not believe a miracle is self-diminishing through use. I remember how impressed I was and how grateful for the personal contact. I wonder why students today don't evidence the same awe toward achievement. This is an age which doesn't refer to the heroes of the past; it barely knows them. That is perhaps why the students so often repeat the past's mistakes. Gravity isn't the only law that they can't repeal. Maybe his disciples didn't know he was more than ordinary. It's more than just the prophet-in-his-area syndrome. Are they so dulled that there is room only for a so-what approach?

We discussed the problem of properly clamping the badly inflamed gallbladder, and he asked if I had ever used his clamp. Never having heard of it, I said I hadn't. After lunch he hustled me through the streets with his arm linked through mine—he was a short, corpulent man, as a number of famous men are. I imagined myself walking with Balzac or Brahms—genius rarely seems to be fitted out with athleticism and comeliness—and he took me into an instrument shop. Have you, he asked the clerk, a Maingot clamp? Yes, sir.

He took it and handed it to me as a gift. The clerk wanted to know whom to bill for it. Why, the surgeon said, Maingot, of course.

I use it. It works efficiently. Sometimes I let a resident use it but I insist on having it returned. I keep it in my locker along with several other instruments I value and keep secure for fear of damage or loss. There are lots of instruments like that, little publicized, and often unknown, but they make a great deal of difference. They save time, and prevent blood loss, and make it simpler to get at the problem, which is what surgery is about.

Surgery is simple, compared to the intricacies of electronic engineering, or the mathematical determinations of astronomers—I see Galileo and Copernicus arriving at concepts more startling and incomprehensible than Harvey's recognition of the circulation of the blood. The fact that we deal with the problems of pain and survival makes surgeons more needed, but not ever arcane. So in improving our techniques we look for better methods, and better methods require improved tools.

I believe in examining other disciplines for ideas. I walk through the aisles of a Woolworth's and pick up and examine kitchen gadgets. I wait for the astonishment of an intern assisting me as I ask the nurse for a spoon—not a euphemism for a complicated device, but an actual spoon. She wants to know if I want a teaspoon or a soupspoon. Not as highly polished and expensive as it would be if made by a surgical supply house, but so long as it can be autoclaved I can use it as it comes from the dime store. I find it useful as a retractor in small incisions in the abdominal wall, for an appendix, or a hernia. It can be contoured to conform to the area I want to hold back. To take fluid from the abdomen or to catch the exudate from a large abscess or the gall from a gallbladder that you want to empty of its stones, I use an ordinary soup ladle. It works, so I use it.

I look in hardware stores for possible conversion of the tools used by other technicians. I watch a carpenter when he comes into my home to work. I watch what the plumber uses.

You see what your mind is prepared for. The problem is that

120

there is too little cross fertilization from one specialty to another. In dentistry they used methyl methacrylate as an adhesive for decades; only recently has it been adapted for use in hip replacements.

Now we have bioengineering, where the experts devise all sorts of new mechanical approaches. In intra-abdominal surgery only the man doing it can think of what he might need to make the task easier. Not that a new tool does more, in the beginning, than create a new problem. One has to learn how to use it. One has to learn how to counter the natural perversity of all inanimate objects. And there still is no substitute, no matter how rarified the instrument, for the opposing thumb.

"So, Charlie," I said to Newman, "let's get these clamps on and line them up."

Newman had been holding the retractor to keep the liver tilted away from the working area. He handed the retractor to me and I handed it to the nurse. He sighed, and opened and closed his fists.

"I couldn't do this operation without you." I said.

"Why do medical students have to suffer to learn?" Newman said.

"That's profound," Spector said. "He's got a hold of something profound there, Dr. Schein,"

"Someday," I said, "you'll tell your students how you held the idiot sticks for old Dr. Schein, and what an experience that was."

"He pulled those retractors with too much force," Spector said."There's some ooze from the liver capsule."

"To be treated by—?" I said to Newman.

"A tourniquet around the spleen?" he said.

"Pressure," I said, ignoring him. It's important to ignore a medical student once in a while. I put a pad down and took Newman's fingers and put them in place and pressed. "Keep it like that."

"For how long?"

"That standard question. Not as deep as a well or as wide as a church door. How long will the operation take, Doctor? The end, Newman, is always—and I say, always—that of the halfway point."

"I don't mind being exploited," Newman said; "what I can't stand is denigration."

"You have to make room for instruction," I said. "I mean, where are you going to put the new information unless you clear a

121

space. Since all we can do now is wait while nature seals, let us be instructive. Spector, tell us about being a superior resident."

"A superior resident," Spector said, "according to a sheet being circulated among the house staff, leaps buildings with a single bound and walks on water. Inferior residents, and medical students, can't recognize the building, and pass rather than walk on the other."

"I saw that sheet," I said. "You can either talk with God or argue with yourself, and lose the argument. But this is a teaching institution. How long should a procedure take? We use a clock on the wall here in the O.R. Some surgeons ought to have a calendar. Or take the surgeon I know who's famous for speed. He was out playing golf one morning and when he returned I asked him how it went and he said pretty good, nine holes in forty-five minutes."

"I think I lost the use of one finger," Newman said.

"Take bleeding," I said. "Do you think George Washington would have lived if Benjamin Rush had not bled him to death as a therapeutic procedure?"

"English law," Newman said, "required sawdust on the floor of the barbershops where surgery was performed."

"In Russia," Spector said, "they use cadaver blood."

I asked the nurse for Sam.

"Sam?" Newman said.

I couldn't be expected to ask a nurse for the twelve-inch-long forceps, so I call it Sam. I took it and told Newman to take his hand away. I lifted away the pad with the instrument. The oozing had stopped.

I put the long intestinal clamps on the bowel. They are curved like a question mark laid on its side. The C portion grasped the end of the stomach behind the clips. The other held the jejunum. I lifted both tissues out of the depth of the abdomen. Suturing will be easier this way. "Hold these," I said to Newman, presenting him with the long handles.

I placed four green towels around to frame the area where we were going to work. The end of the stomach and the end of the small intestine were now laid out and clamped in place, separated from all else, about to be joined together. In sickness and in health. To the marriage of true minds admit no impediment—Even surgeons ramble in their heads.

122

With the field isolated, I was about to ask for the silk suture for the outer layer when Mrs. Ellis came in and stood uncertainly at the door. "Doctor—?"

"What's the matter, Mrs. Ellis?"

"It's Dr. Kommer across the hall. He's doing a colectomy and there's trouble in there. The patient's already had four units of blood and it hasn't stopped and—"

"I can't go in unless he asks for me."

"I know, but he's sick. He's sitting on a stool with his head down and the resident is asking for you."

"Spector," I said. "The great moment in the life of the understudy. Today you become a star."

"Gee," Spector said.

"You want to do the anastomosis, don't you?"

"I sure do."

"Start it. I'll be right back."

18

The circumstances in which one surgeon is called in to another man's case usually fall into these categories: There is an unusual manifestation of a disease—something is bent in an odd way, there is a bizarre coupling, the plumbing doesn't go in the usual direction. Or maybe there is something that was obvious, and turned into something else. I recall a beautiful example of that. A woman with cancer of the neck had been operated on and her condition ameliorated. Then she came back with a mass in the abdomen and food didn't get through. I was called in to do what I could with what was obviously a hopeless spread of the original disease. Her family was prepared for the worst. I found the abdominal tumor was simply an enlarged uterus with simple fibroids, benign and correctable. That was the mass. The obstruction was an ulcer, again correctable, and the hopeless original diagnosis became a curable condition. Hurray for surgeons.

Sometimes another surgeon will call you in to show off something he has done—an odd anastomosis, or vascular surgery where the newly directed flow of blood can be dramatically satisfying. Or it can happen that a colleague needs a corroborating decision, usually when he fears the result is going to be poor and he wants later to be able to say, Well, I called in Doctor So-and-so, who agreed that this was the best procedure.

But rarely are you called in because somebody is in serious trouble. That was the case now. The O.R. was a bloody mess.

Dr. Kommer was sitting, head down, on a stool. The anesthetist was squeezing the hanging plastic bag to get blood quickly into the patient on the table. The resident and his assistant had their heads low over the abdominal cavity. Lap pads and towels were bloody.

One assistant had some blood on his glasses where it had spurted. There was an obvious uncontrolled hemorrhage. I asked the anesthetist about the condition of the patient. In a moment I would learn from the surgeons what was happening in the belly. Only the anesthetist could tell me what was happening to the patient. "He's on his fifth unit of blood. BP 90, his pulse is going at 130."

I asked the resident what had happened.

"We went in for a tumor of the colon. It turned out to be something in back of it. It's poorly defined. Everything was going well from the front but when we tried to mobilize the damn thing from behind we got into something and it's been bleeding like hell. We must have torn something big."

"Take a lap pad, put it down where it's bleeding, and hold it. Press down, just hold it.

I went to Kommer. "What happened, Arthur?"

"I got dizzy. I can't see straight. Maybe it's some acute viral thing. I was okay when I started but—I know I can't talk intelligently now. Just get this thing under control, will you?"

I changed gown and gloves. I did it slowly, deliberately, to give me time to think. Since the tumor was in back of the colon, and an effort had obviously been made to remove it along with the capsule—not always a wise primary maneuver because a bulky tumor in that position can be adherent to a large blood vessel, and it might have been better to have done it from within, like taking out the substance of an orange and leaving the rind—the extent and spurt of the bleeding indicated a tear in the vena cava. The area had to be pinpointed and the hole closed. This is a surgical rubato, to get quickly to the next action.

I wanted the pad pressed in place for at least ten minutes. Meanwhile the blood pressure had to be brought up, which meant at least two more units. When the anesthetist said the pressure had reached 110 I had the assistant use a sucker to catch the seepage around the pad. I then carefully lifted it. It was, in a more dramatic and serious way, a repetition of what we had just done in the other room with Padget, whose liver had been breeched by the retractor. I asked for a sponge stick and when the blood rushed up through the now-defined hole I got the sponge down over the bleeding hole in the vena cava. I asked for a vascular clamp, which by its delicacy and shape doesn't damage the blood vessel, while it excludes the part to be sewn.

Again it was clamp, cut, and tie. What surgery is about.

Hemorrhage is uncontrolled bleeding. It usually doesn't happen because every sizable blood vessel is clamped before being cut. Halsted of Johns Hopkins once said hemorrhage was the only way a patient can attest to a surgeon's incompetence. But nothing should come as a surprise. If you drive a car in the winter you have to be prepared for a patch of ice.

You're confident if you have been there before. You put in the cork, and you make up the blood loss. If there's too much lost too quickly the kidney suffers, the most sensitive organ in the abdomen. Only the brain, which can be permanently damaged after three minutes of inadequate blood, is more critical. In this case, with the blood pressure not having fallen below 90, I was not worried; that pressure was enough to keep the blood flowing through the kidneys.

I clamped around the bleeding site and when all the blood had been sucked up we had a dry field and the problem was isolated. A two-millimeter hole. Now exposed and controlled. The rest was easy—I sewed up the rent with fine silk. Took off the clamp. It was dry. The emergency was over. The hemorrhage controlled. So what else is new?

When it is said that life hangs on a thread that is exactly what happened. A half inch of silk thread and three knots.

Dr. Kommer looked up. I asked him if he felt better.

"I do. Now, what happened?"

"A hole in the cava. We got it sewed up, everything's okay. You need any more help? You want me to finish, you want me to stay and help?"

"I'm all right, now. Thanks. I'll talk to you later."

I nodded, and went back to my own case.

I felt good about having done this. The end which is the purpose of the beginning and middle. I had been away from Padget for only fifteen minutes. It had taken me a lifetime to get here. Like the musician who practices forever and then auditions for three minutes. That's all it takes for the maestro to know if he's good.

People fall sick in patterns, but the treatment is always the same, and one longs for a gallbladder shaped a little differently or a spleen out of place. But you can't wait for the unusual, so you have to see the extraordinary in the commonplace. The French Impressionist painters saw it in flowers and street scenes. The musical ear detects it in a sequence of two notes, certainly in three. The sensitive surgical sense detects it in the manner of presentation of the disease process and its variants. Make no mistake about it, there is nothing morbid in the intellectual excitement generated in the understanding of disease. It is like the painter's cubism, the musician's atonality. The more one knows, the greater the incidence of variations within the pattern. One gets excited by the patterns and their variants.

The dream of the medical student who sees himself rising in the theater as the call comes from the stage—that's real. It happens. And young doctors like it. No matter how solemn they have always been, no matter that the frock coat and high hat have been discarded—perhaps regrettably—so a doctor dresses like everyone else—there are still those times when only he has the knowledge and skill to continue a life.

The doctor and the patient. I had gone into medicine because I thought that in this world of indifferent machines, anti-intellectualism, and profit-oriented businessmen, the doctor could somehow continue as supreme individualist, taking care of one sick person at a time. The right to be odd, if you felt like it. The skill for which there would always be a need, hence mobility, hence independence. The monk with special privileges. Universality, to be able to walk into any hospital in any country in the world. The link with scholarship, the recognition of never knowing it all, which gives living a special quality of never being able to fill the glass. Not that there are not smug doctors, as there are fumbling presidents and uninformed engineers.

Of course, it's a delusion. You can do the most complicated procedure on a patient and all she will remember of her hospital experience is that once her bedpan came late or her meal was cold. The truth is that doctors are never really independent. Which is why surgeons are laconic. Your master can be the difficult patient, the minor hospital official, a member of your own surgical team, the operating-room nurse, or the referring doctor. Regional legalisms

127

can prevent you from practicing your profession away from your home base. Colleagues can become ruthless competitors. Yet the diseases are the same.

Patient and doctor and a fee for service. Ineluctably eroded now by third-party payment, which is good for insurance carriers, whose computers, free from telephones, pain, and gratitude, can estimate only code names and numbers. If fees are set in a standard way by insurance companies, how are they to recognize good medicine from bad, skilled surgeons from the barely competent? The patient has no way of knowing that the bedside manner which is so comforting can be a mask for ignorance, while the terse and unfriendly practitioner has fashioned a miracle.

Medicine is becoming controlled by whatever agency can capture the patient. The specialist, the trade union group, the prepaid medical plan, the civil service fringe benefit. The doctor is conceived of as a purchasable commodity. And the incentive for excellence is being lost.

I used to covet M.D. license plates. Now I don't want to be identified. I don't want to be a target for the addict because doctors carry drugs, or the thief because the doctor is supposed to carry large sums of money. I used to leave my name at the box office when I went to the theater. Now I wait until I get out to call my office. I am tired of the hundreds of movies the endings of which I have never seen. I no longer care to be identified as a doctor outside the professional arena. Lawyers and insurance companies have contributed to my desire for anonymity.

We have lost the security of small objectives. To (in the words of my young daughter) just fix people up when they get broken.

Someone said the ideal way to be a surgeon was to know how and be able to do it but not have to.

All of which I sometimes believe, all of which makes me angry, but none of which I allow to interfere in the positive euphoria engendered by the assistance I was able to give Kommer, and the benefit Padget was receiving, and the instruction being given to Newman and Spector. Because if Abraham was successful in bargaining with God for the preservation of Gomorrah if he could find ten decent men living there, I know at least that many decent physicians, and I have had a thousand times that number of happy patients. I'm happy as a doctor. I want to continue that life. I'd do it again. There's a reason to get up in the morning and an earned fatigue that makes insomnia incomprehensible.

But now I'm beginning to understand the old man in Cleveland, the man from whom I learned the excitement of chest surgery. There was a dark heavy rain. We were finishing our second cup of coffee. The case was behind us. He said, "After forty years it would be good to know something different. I can't do anything else that someone would pay for. That's the price of being an expert. It limits you. Take my advice, learn something else. After you learn 90 percent of surgery is it worthwhile spending a lifetime to learn the other 5 percent? Because you can't ever learn more than that."

Hospital practice is impersonal. There are young doctors impressed with the romance of ghetto medicine and perhaps they will change our world. In my generation I knew a man who made house calls. Once he knocked on a door. It was opened, he went in and was hit on the head. They took his black bag and his wallet. You would think after that, that he would refuse house calls. He continued to go out. And once again he was hit on the head and they took his money and his new black bag and this time they took his automobile. Then he stopped making house calls. He closed his office and tried to get a job. There was little call for an elderly general practitioner. His savings were used up and he committed suicide.

The moral of that story is you can't go back and what happens if there's no place to go forward? I was an idealist in medical school. We were all idealists.

After my residencies were over I wanted to go into an independent private practice. Free of the hospital. Was I naïve or stupid? I had had enough of going from fifteen dollars a month as an intern to thirty-five dollars in my third year. In my sixth year I was paid $105 in biweekly installments. Was it broken up that way to forestall any single episode of reckless spending? In the hospital I didn't know I was impoverished. I didn't know anyone who lived differently. They gave me a room, board, laundry, and a schedule so fatiguing that there was little need for a social life. I deferred it.

Now I wanted the freedom to be unadministered, and unscheduled on a typewritten sheet that had my name along the side with the date of being on night and weekend call. I had had enough of stiff, starched white uniforms and of being supervised, however benevolently; I wanted to be free.

I came back to New York to go into private surgical practice. I had been training in hospitals for six years after medical school. I owned lots of books and some records, principally chamber music and lieder.

I should have recognized the omen. It was the blizzard of December 1947.

19

For six years hospitals had supplied all my needs. First at Bellevue and then in Cleveland, I was provided with a place to sleep, food, laundry—all the basics with opportunity to fill in the fringe requirements of companionship, and night-long Lennie and George talks of how it was going to be. Now in this prophetic blizzard, I was going back to New York without friends or money, and I understood why an infant's first reaction after being yanked from the womb is to scream with fright.

You took for granted that at night you would have a warm bed, and a pair of clean overstarched pants to pull on when you got up, and a place to sit and eat three hot meals with a fourth always available around midnight. One wing of the hospital consisted of staff quarters, each small room with a single bed, sink, dresser, desk, bookcase, closet—and a telephone fixed over the bed without extension cord or an adjustment volume. A quickly learned reflex was arm over the head and receiver brought down to the ear while the eyes stayed shut. On each floor were communal showers and toilets. One of the privileges of senior resident status was a room with your own shower. Once a week you put your laundry in a purse-string canvas bag outside the door. You made your own bed, but the room was cleaned.

Interns and residents are most concerned with the disease, less with the patient, and least with the relatives of the patient. So at visiting hours you went to your own room, or the lounge, or the X-ray department. I liked to read films; I sat with the radiologist or went through the X-ray museum where the unusual cases were kept on file, and I learned a great deal about reading the films for myself.

Private practice was going to mean having also to deal with

relatives. The old man was experienced. He initiated me into the principles and practice of relativity. Laymen, he said, can be given utterly meaningless statements about the patient, as long as they are delivered in a straightforward and professional manner.

"How's he doing?"

"If he doesn't get complications we have nothing to worry about."

"Why is he still running a temperature?"

"He's got congestion."

"What's going to happen?"

"If it goes away everything will be fine. If it doesn't go away we'll have to take some other tests."

"What kind of tests?"

"X rays and blood tests."

"When he finally gets out of the hospital will he be okay?"

"Ninety percent of patients with this operation do very well. But people are not all alike. I can't quite answer but we'll see how he comes along."

"Can this condition recur?"

"We'll just have to keep an eye on him."

The evasiveness has a purpose. Most of the time you don't have exact answers, but the questions call for answers. And you always provide yourself with an exit should the need arise. Besides, relatives don't want specifics, they want reassurance; although the more intelligent know your answers are meaningless they feel better without knowing why.

In the hospital you aren't interested in being identified as the patient's doctor. You're filling the gas tank, repairing the shoe —you're learning a trade. In private practice you're the doctor, you want all the credit, you're the one who is going to be paid. As a house staff member you aren't involved with the social problems; in private practice when the patient leaves, you remain his doctor. In the hospital the patient who comes in as an emergency or for elective surgery without an attending gets special attention only if he has an interesting profession (once a gunsmith came in and the resident was an enthusiastic gun collector and he looked forward to a subsequent relationship of mutual involvement) or if the disease is a rare one or if the patient is a pretty girl. Otherwise if the I. V. is uncomfortable the patient is made to believe that's the way it's supposed to be.

In the hospital the surgeon says, Put him under and open the belly and I'll come in. In private practice the anesthetist is notified not to put the patient asleep until the surgeon comes in and says hello.

To the resident the patient is the big hernia in 204. To the private physician he's Mr. Smith who is the brother-in-law of the gallbladder he took out a year ago.

Originally only poor patients went to the hospital. The hospital was a place where infections were rampant; you got sicker in hospitals. You still pick up irrelevant illnesses in hospitals. Rich people were operated on at home. Recently one of the Georges had his lung removed in Buckingham Palace.

When a resident fumbles an endotracheal tube because he's making too many passes he keeps going until he gets into the trachea. A private physician lets him try once or twice but then takes over himself because he doesn't want his private patient with an unnecessary sore throat.

When a ward patient is discharged: Resident: "Make arrangements with the nurse for clinic appointments. She'll tell you where to go." Private doctor: "I want to see you in my office in two weeks." If the resident's day at the clinic does not coincide with the arrangements made for the patient they may never see each other again. The man in private practice gets involved with the patient and his family in an association that may go on for years.

What I was faced with now, traveling in the storm, going into private practice, was the necessity to learn the art of dealing with patients as people, and especially the relatives of patients. I would most of the time not be interested in them aside from the surgical situation, but I would have to learn how to avoid presenting a detached attitude. I would have to acquire new affability. I discovered, much later, that in each of my patients, no matter what their social position or intellectual attainment, there was something new to be learned, some advantage in the relationship. Detachment had limited opportunity, but it was protective. I was to learn the hurt of sensitivity. Immunity is the failure to respond. In disease it maintains life; in the social situation it's death.

133

A surgeon has to work. A surgeon needs to work. Despite the fees the public hears about, what is not known is that if a surgeon could not earn anything from the use of his skills he would have to keep working for nothing. So that's the way I began private practice, by working for nothing.

I had an uncle in practice in a small town. He had offered to take me in, to introduce me to the realities, to get me started. He began by buying me my first car.

I didn't know how to drive. I had been a student for twenty-five years. I knew only that which came from books, lectures, the preceptor system in the operating rooms. I knew a great deal about the pathology and surgery of diseased individuals, but I knew almost nothing about what they did for a living. I had never tried a martini. Outside of medicine I was a true primitive.

I took lessons. I learned to drive like a doctor. It did not on a lonely road seem logical to me that the lines dividing the lanes were not to be used as a straddling device to keep the car from swerving. I wasn't self-conscious. I never believed that the blaring horn behind was sounding for me, or that the contorted face of the driver as he passed was the result of my ineptness. I wouldn't move out of the left lane to aid the honking idiot behind me to exceed the speed limit.

On the second day of ownership, I backed the car into a fire hydrant and crumpled the fender. I didn't have the money to pay for the repair. I had to borrow it from my uncle.

He said, "Clarence, you have great hands in the O.R. Why do they turn into wood when you get behind a steering wheel?"

"I don't know. I am coordinated and intelligent. I get the feeling there's some kind of animistic malevolence in that pile of machinery. Do you think it's possible that automobiles can hate?"

"If you can't drive you can't work. So drive better."

My uncle was a practical man. Over the next six months I kept coming to him with unsolvable problems which he beat into unpalatable fact. "Waiting rooms are for waiting. Who cares if you're angry, insulted, and your ass has fallen asleep? Not only don't they know what a great surgeon you are, but if they knew they wouldn't want the competition. Patience. They never taught you patience in all those fancy hospitals you went to for training?"

They had never taught me that between the patient and my

134

skills was a moat of self-serving and protective doctors whose purpose was to keep me from working. In that avuncular community I found myself like a man on a train going in the wrong direction and I didn't know how to get off.

I got a temporary appointment in the local hospital because my uncle had been practicing there for twenty-five years and I was ostensibly coming in as his assistant. Therefore I assumed that when I got up in the morning I had someplace to go. But there was no ward service. The library there was no better than I had collected myself over the years, and besides the door was always locked, with the key needing to be obtained from a grumpy nursing supervisor. What one was expected to do was sit in the doctors' lounge to make one's presence known. I went there, and was embarrassed by my inability to participate in the conversations about golf scores, income-tax evasion—I had no income—and snide remarks about those doctors not present. Nobody invited me to lunch.

My sole surgical activity was to assist my uncle in some of his operations, assistance he did not need but he charitably paid me, and for the rest of the time I had nothing to do. I felt my skills rusting and my mind atrophying. I felt I knew more than the professionals around me, but they depersonalized me out of existence. I went from being referred to as my uncle's assistant to his nephew—as our relationship was made known—I became aware of the routes or referral by which these surgeons made their living and it was clear after a while—it would have been clearer if I had been a shade more sophisticated—that there was no way I could break into that daisy chain, unless, if I waited long enough, someone would die; and even then I suspected they would simply close the gap. No entrance. Exit to the right.

So I helped my uncle, who overpaid me for the help, which is the only way I had pocket money.

Occasionally I was given an emergency case. The nurse who ran that service fed the cases to whoever was supposed to be on duty that month. After a while I found out that the cases I ran down to take care of were derelicts or youngsters with no means and no insurance. Insurance cases always seemed to be given to one of the other staff members, whether he was on call or not.

My uncle, the practical practicing doctor, said, "Clarence, what

135

the hell do you expect? That nurse grew up in this town, she knows all the other men, and maybe they show her a small token of gratitude. Why the hell should she channel a profitable case to you?"

"I don't understand this method of practicing medicine."

"Try."

"What kind of future do I have here?"

"Who knows? But you have to wait. You have to get to know these fellows. It takes time."

"But I can do things they can't. Nobody here can work in the chest."

"Listen to me, Clarence. The way things are, not the way they ought to be or the way you think they should be. Nobody knows what you can do, because you haven't shown them. They won't give you a chance to show them. They deal in simple logic. How can a kid just out of his residencies know more than a man who's been at it for twenty-five years? So they won't let you work. But suppose they get a case they can't handle, and you can? Then they'll send the case to somebody far away, so there can't be a question of their inadequacy coming home to roost."

"I like the metaphor. But I have to work. What do I have to do?"

"I told you."

"You told me to be patient. Patience isn't working. I have to work. I have to have a reason to get up in the morning."

"Then you ought to try for an appointment at one of the city hospitals. You won't get paid, but you'll get cases."

"Maybe you're right. Maybe I ought to try that."

20

What I was faced with was the medical lie. I had lived the myth.

As a student, as a resident learning as much as I could, I was sure that upon completion of my training I would encounter a world of waiting patients and agreeable colleagues.

The reality was that nobody wanted me. My uncle was totally without sympathy for my naïveté. "You're pushing for a seat on a bench that is already overcrowded. If there's room for your ass somebody else's ass on the other end is going onto the floor. He's been at it for twenty-five years, and he doesn't want to wind up sitting on the floor. Furthermore, he doesn't deserve to be pushed off."

I still didn't believe it. It didn't make sense. Certainly there are more sick people than doctors to take care of them. Newspapers don't lie. I was a well-trained surgeon. Surgery changes all the time; there were new procedures and new methods and I knew what they were. Any hospital ought to be glad to have me.

It wasn't even a question of money. Certainly I wanted to support myself, but beyond that was the need to keep working. A surgeon gets rusty very fast.

So I applied for staff privileges to a large city hospital. I offered my services, for free, to the charity patients of a large city. And I couldn't get it. It was an exclusive club.

I now understand about operating-room doors. They have no knobs. You have to kick or push your way in.

I waited in other surgeons' waiting rooms. As my uncle pointed out, that's what waiting rooms were for. I was greeted with affability and smoothness. "I've heard good things about you, Clarence. I'm sure we can find room for you, later."

Clarence. I had never met this man before. He had long thin white fingers, so I almost believe the story of the white-gloved barracks inspector. Curly, in *Of Mice and Men,* keeping his hands Vaselined in gloves. This doctor was chief of service and I went to see him in his Park Avenue office. He made all staff appointments.

"Of course, Clarence, we'll have to bring up the question of your appointment to the medical committee. We ought to get it through in six months."

I could hang out a shingle, display my license, go into general practice. That was allowed. But a surgeon needs a hospital. I was willing to work for nothing, and now, smiling, he said my application would be completed in six months. He could have picked up a phone and given temporary privileges immediately. But he didn't. Why should he? I was just another resident now out. He was very friendly. He said, "Goodbye, Clarence, you'll be hearing from us."

A sniper gets on top of a building and shoots people indiscriminately. Somebody plants a bomb in a department store. When he can manage it, a doctor charges large fees for his services. Maybe it's all part of the same thing, the kind of frustration against the realities of the world that grips you by the throat and demands an out. The alternative to doing one's thing. But I was a long way from charging anyone, and I didn't know anything about bombs or guns.

"Be patient," said my uncle.

"I'm not trying to build Rome," I said. "Four years in the belly, and a year in the chest. For what?"

"We all went through it. Why should everything be made simple for you? These guys who run the services sweated their way in. Many of them—maybe most—learned their surgery by watching, and then trying it themselves. You expect them to bow before some academic snotnose, to share their pie?"

"I don't want their pie, and I promise always to wear a mask. I just want to be used."

"Patience," my uncle said.

Granted that I was uninformed and without business sense even for those days. Residents today are not slapped about unprepared for the realities. We were mostly a monastic group apprenticed to poverty, obedience, and the pursuit of learning how. I judge this

138

generation to be less orthodox; they know what page of the newspaper has the stock market quotations, they know in advance what square footage of office space they require and what it costs, dedicated to the principle that the pursuit of personal happiness is being on call one night a week. They begin to set up their future in their last year. Groups are formed, community opportunities are investigated, there has been a certain amount of preparatory moonlighting. They talk shamelessly with each other about the business of medicine. How could I have been so witless?

I kept going to the city hospital, just to have a place to go. I became very familiar with the corridors, and the emergency rooms. Finally one of the attendings said, "Schein, if you like, you can sit in on the conferences." So I sat and listened to discussions of cases.

I longed for strings to pull, I had letters of recommendation but no one to show them to. Six months was forever.

Meanwhile, I looked into the available voluntary hospitals. There were two hospitals then, and one had as a chief of medicine the doctor who had brought me into this world. I went to see him, and he sent me to one of the heads of the surgical department. I got "Clarenced" right away, and was permitted to see at least twenty-five teeth, and I was told regretfully how there was just no room for another man.

Municipal hospitals, voluntaries, proprietaries. The last is run by doctors for private profit. No charity cases. The city hospital has no private cases, and the staff surgeons were, then, not paid. The voluntary hospital is in the middle. Run by a group—religious, business, cultural—not for profit and accepting both private and charity patients.

At the time I began you were prepared to donate a percentage of your time to the free clinic. That was how you repaid the hospital for allowing you use of their hardware and personnel. Today, you are expected to be on call for emergency-ward duty.

Nobody likes night duty, and nobody remains enthusiastic about abscesses or gunshot wounds or skin lacerations. What the surgeon looks for is the "interesting" case. Anything that's different, complicated, impossible. What the doctors got from the city hospital was the chance to learn from the poor and transmit results of their education to their private patients. After a while I was allowed to do the scutwork. Both hospitals called me out at night, and at both hospitals I worked in the emergency rooms. I was working at the level of a third-year resident.

My uncle said I was doing fine.

None of the philosophy of medicine I had learned was true. In medical school I had been taught to believe the myths of our heritage. My teachers there didn't know they were lying; they had never been in private practice. They didn't know the truths of protecting your domain, keeping out the competition.

The other of the two voluntary hospitals was famous as a treatment and holding center for chronic cases, and was just beginning to open up an area for private patients and acute illness. Here was a chance for me. A former professor at Bellevue secured the necessary introductions and I was added to the staff. This meant that I could hang around the hospital and, if I had one, bring in a private patient.

In Westchester a patient came in who had no money and a tumor in his lung. They had no facilities there for chest surgery, and since nobody wanted the impoverished patient, I had him to myself. I took out his lung, and he did well. The residents there were friendly and happy to see me get a start. The next case I got was a patient of my uncle's who asked if there was any surgical intervention that was possible for high blood pressure. My uncle said there was an operation he knew of, which he didn't do, but which his nephew could.

Since my first case had gone well, what happened after that didn't matter. And here was my second case in a month. I was a success. I was a young surgeon on his way up. Again the facilities for chest work were there, and I did an operation called a thoracolumbar sympathectomy, an operation since given up. The theory was that removing the chain of nerves in the thorax and back of abdomen relieved the vascular spasm causing extreme hypertension. I am now old enough to have seen the beginning and demise of this procedure. Once an operative procedure gets into a reliable medical journal it can take as long as a generation to establish whether the operation has any value. Drugs now do better what that operation was supposed to accomplish.

My third operation was the first referral from my peers, and in an area which was awakening my interest. It was a Sunday afternoon, and I was playing tennis on the hospital court. A lady of fifty-five had been feeling ill and was told by a doctor in her building that she ought to get into the hospital. Having been treated in the past by the chief of medicine, she called the administrator's office and asked for one of the chief surgeons to come and see her. The man I was playing with, on the administration staff, suggested I go to see the woman; my tennis was mediocre anyway.

"Didn't she ask for a chief surgeon?"

"I so dub you."

"I don't have any suitable clothes."

We went inside and one of the residents offered me his father-in-law's suit, which he had inherited. I got into it—it almost fit—and went out to see the patient. I had no doctor's bag; I had rubber gloves in my pocket in case an internal examination was required. There is a surgical maxim that if you don't put your finger in the rectum you put your foot in the diagnosis.

The husband and daughter were waiting. I looked very young. The husband said, "Are you one of the chief surgeons?"

"Isn't that whom you asked for?" I said.

He took me into the bedroom. On examination there was no problem: the woman had a large inflamed gallbladder and it was equally obvious she was in mild congestive heart failure. From a diagnostic point of view she was the classic case presented to a third-year medical student.

I told her she had to come into the hospital and would probably need an operation. She agreed to come into the hospital but wasn't all that sure I could be trusted. I called the cardiologist, who remembered the patient, and he arranged to meet her at the hospital. She was taken by cab with her husband and daughter. I could have taken her in my car, but remembered some of the wisdom I was fast accumulating. Never take the patient in your car (certain emergency situations omitted, of course). Too much opportunity for relatives to quiz you. I was learning the tangential approach.

The cardiologist examined her, agreed with my diagnosis, took me aside. "Can you do it?"

"Yes."

He went back to the patient and her husband and said she needed to be operated on and that Dr. Schein was a very competent surgeon.

I took out a gallbladder inflamed and with stones, and she made an uneventful recovery.

Five years later the lady died from progressive cardiac deterioration—today her mitral valve could have been replaced safely. The intern who assisted me has become a well-known cardiac surgeon. The administrator who sent me on the case is now running a large hospital in Connecticut in association with Yale. And I am still removing gallbladders.

This was my first private case. The administrator, intern, and I sat around after the operation and discussed the fee. I said I had no idea what to charge. The intern insisted, "You did save her life. I would suggest a fee of ten thousand dollars."

"That seems a little high," the administrator said.

"How much is a life worth?" said the intern.

I thought I ought to talk to my uncle. I asked for a fee of two hundred and fifty dollars, which was paid out to me at the rate of twenty-five dollars a month. I was very happy to get it.

I remembered a guide to medical practice from some Arabian treatise of the eleventh century: Charge high fees, for what is done gratis is assumed to be of little value. Let your practice be confined to the rich, for they are grateful and will reward you for what you have done, whereas the common person will resent whatever you charge. But I was still at the stage of being confused at getting paid for what I liked to do.

I had now done three successful cases and I was ready to branch out. I went back to my other voluntary hospital and waited. I didn't get anything to do. I spent a lot of time listening to the reminiscences of the chief of surgery. From what I gathered, his cases were mostly blunders which recovered with diligent postoperative care and a lot of luck. He was a venerable looking old man trained in the preceptor days. All he lacked was the ability to make a decision, and the technical dexterity to excute his assistant's advice.

The doctor has neither more nor less virtue than the local grocer, but he has more opportunities to practice it. I felt virtuous, but lacked examples to prove it. I grew despondent three or four times a day and considered the examples of famous men who, having studied medicine, went into something else. Chekhov, Keats, Conan Doyle, Rabelais, Oliver Goldsmith, Maugham, Cronin.

I had been trained in thoracic surgery, although I was becoming particularly interested in the abdomen, and one day a man came in from the clinic with an obvious cancer of the esophagus. He had trouble swallowing. The diagnosis was easy because the X ray was typical. A biopsy had been taken and it proved to be negative for cancer.

I told the chief that the biopsy had to be wrong. I said, "You let the biopsy be done by the E.N.T. men, who aren't going to follow through. The biopsy ought to be done by the man who is going to operate."

"Negative is negative."

"I don't believe it. The X-ray diagnosis is obvious. There's an obstruction at the lower end of the esophagus and the configuration indicates a malignancy."

"Okay," the chief said, "you take another biopsy."

For the first and I hope the last time in my life, I wanted to see confirmation of the unfortunate diagnosis. And that was the way it came out. The chief said, "I'll do it, you assist."

I look back now on my temerity and brashness. I told the older, successful man that I would not assist him, but I would be happy to do the operation and permit him to assist me. I was not, I sensed, going to be popular.

I said, "I have been trained to do this kind of thing. Furthermore, I think I am the only man in the hospital well enough trained to do it. And if you don't let me do it, there is no point to my being here at all."

Instead of kicking me down the stairs, he agreed.

I went in through the chest, a procedure new to the surgeons there. I found a resectable tumor, and all went well postoperatively. The operation was talked about. And it brought me to the attention of the chief of obstetrics and gynecology, a man I knew by reputation, a man who might have delivered me—so my mother told me later—had my parents only been, at the time, able to afford the fee.

Dr. Rongy was in the last trimester of his active career. He had established his reputation, and was now old enough to be free of envy and interested in the welfare of the institution. In his own department he had sent men to train elsewhere, to get other points of view and bring them back. He wanted his hospital to develop. He recognized the hemophilia of inbreeding which was sapping the vitality of the surgical staff.

"Where is your office, Dr. Schein?"

I told him I was living with an uncle and sharing his quarters.

"Wouldn't you like a place of your own?"

"Yes. I would indeed."

He took me to his suite of rooms in mid-Manhattan, a side entrance off Central Park West. It was like Harley Street with a touch of Beverly Hills, I thought, never having been in either of those places. The waiting room was spacious, paneled, with paintings—not prints—on the walls. His consultation room had an oriental rug on the floor, a huge desk, a wall of books. A place to awaken awe and respect in a patient. The sanctum of a professor. It was the sort of place that, one day, I might want for myself.

Rongy said, "I do not operate much anymore. I am here only some mornings, and the place is going to waste. Why shouldn't a bright young doctor like yourself get the benefit of these surroundings? You could build a practice from an office like this."

I didn't say anything. I couldn't.

"You could pay," he said, "maybe, say, sixty dollars a month?"

Even in 1949 a fair rent would have been two hundred.

"And I will ask my nurse to work with you as you need her, and in the beginning, until you are established, I will meet all of her salary."

About nine months after that the benevolent man died, and I found a colleague to share the office with me. I practiced there for twenty years.

21

In the corridor, where the scrub sinks were, Fisher had been following events through the side window. Surgeons are an abrasive lot who don't compliment their fellows when a case goes well but want to know everything about the mishaps. Fisher thrived on it, and remembered the details. He had a lesser recall for their successes.

"What was the matter with Arthur?"

"I don't know. But he's all right now."

"What happened?"

"They got into bleeding when they were taking the tumor off the cava."

Better him than me, was the grimaced reaction. And he went back to scrubbing his chewed-off fingernails.

Operating-room doors have no knobs. I kicked my way in and changed gown and gloves. Spector was suturing and Newman was being allowed to tie knots. I asked where Spector was at.

"We've got everything walled off, good exposure, I've just put in the outer layer of the gastrojejunostomy."

The end of Padget's duodenum was permanently closed off. The stomach was temporarily clipped closed. Now that part of the stomach had to be mouth opened into the jejunum. This was like attaching the pipe under the sink to the curved section around the trap. It is no accident that plumbing and surgery have much in common.

I went to change gown and gloves. Spector and Newman wanted to know what had happened in the other O.R. and I told them.

"Did you tell your bleeding stories?" Spector said.

145

"What's that?" Newman asked.

"You know Schein says all bleeding stops if you hold a pad on long enough. Evans the neurosurgeon once opened up a large venous sinus in the head. The kind that's fragile and full of blood and it can go like an open faucet. He slapped a pad on it and told the assisting resident to hold it and Evans went out to lunch."

"You're putting me on," Newman said.

"True story," I said.

"Evans came back after lunch," Spector continued, "and peeled off the pad while the resident stood looking at his hand, which had turned into a claw, and, pleased that the bleeding had stopped, Evans said, 'You see what a couple of tunafish sandwiches can do?' "

"Stories?" Newman said.

"Time in the O.R. moves slowly," Spector said. "What do you do while you're waiting for the pressure pad to work? Schein tells stories, and asks questions. How much blood does a man have?"

"All med students know basic things like that," Newman retorted.

"Do they?" Spector said. "In the days bleeding was done therapeutically when did you stop?"

"When?" Newman said.

"When the patient fainted."

"Which vein did you use?"

"Which?"

"According to Hippocrates the vein that is closest to the site of the illness."

"I'll tell you the truth," Newman said. "I don't care much for all this bloody talk."

"Remember what the man said," Spector said, "the blood on the floor isn't yours. It comes in bottles."

"In hara-kiri," I said, as the nurse pulled off my gown and gloves and got me into a new set, "what were they after with their transverse stab about the umbilicus?"

"What?" Newman said.

"The idea is to slash the aorta. Like the matador in a clean kill of the bull, always the aorta," I said.

Surgeons move about the patient on the operating table in a choreographed fashion akin to the waltz of wooing insects. The

146

patient is the fixed point. To his right stands the surgeon, across from him the first assistant flanked by the nurse, to the surgeon's left the second assistant. If a resident is to do the operation the attending surgeon moves to the patient's left without the need to discuss what is to be done. A resident anxious to do a procedure will sometimes try to assume the prominent right position at the beginning to force tacit permission. Spector was now on the right, Newman on the left. If I were to allow Spector to continue I would assume Newman's position, and send Newman to the other side.

I looked at what Spector had done. He had aligned the end of Padget's stomach to the curve of small bowel with silk sutures. The next step would be to make the actual opening, the anastomosis, the mouth-to-mouth.

"Why," I said to Newman, "silk sutures?"

"Why not?" Newman said.

He was not, I decided, impressed enough with the mystique of the surgeon's world.

"Because," I said, "this joining now is going to be forever. The silk will not be absorbed. You remember, of course, our discussion about stomach operations in the past being considered impossible because suture material would have been digested."

"Silk," Newman said. "Because it's permanent."

"Very good," I said. "Paul, I don't like what you did."

"What do you mean?" Spector said.

"If you'll notice," I said, looking inside Padget, "the front part of the clamp holding the jejunum must have slipped a little, so that the right side is three millimeters lower than the left."

"I see that now. What difference does it make?"

"Maybe none," I said. "But it's less than perfect, and I don't want to let it go. We know that Mother Nature is a bitch. If things can go wrong they will. If something goes wrong later this may be the cause. The alignment will not be absolutely straight. It's not your fault, you put the sutures in perfectly. But it's evidence of maladroit coapting of tissue. Why should you have a bumpy scar?

"What you overlooked was the bevel slipping off the end of the clamp. Again the natural perversity of inanimate objects. Suppose this were your own case, in your own town, and you had to see this patient every day, and you asked him how he was eating, and he said everything was all right but, and you thought there was a remote possibility that the reason for the but was your bad joint—would you sleep well? Most postoperative complications are started in the operating room. You wouldn't let an ooze go, you wouldn't sneeze into a wound, something like this is easily controllable, so shouldn't we do it again? Newman, should it be done over?"

"It looks all right to me," Newman said.

"What do you say, Spector? If it were your case, would you do it over?"

He hesitated. I worried about him.

"Nobody would ever know," I said. "But you would know."

I had decided to let Spector finish the case. I went to take over Newman's position.

Padget assumed I was going to do him skin to skin. Patients never know who does the operation. A scissors can't work with one blade only. An operation is a team affair.

The best place to have an operation performed is in a teaching institution, yet to teach is to let someone else do part of the job.

When I was in training the old man started by letting me do parts. In a bilateral hernia I, on the left side of the table, would do one side after he had done the other. In hysterectomies he would do one tube and ovary, and I would do the other. Mirror-image surgery, the best teaching process. Yet the patient didn't know who I was, and the old man was his surgeon, the one doing the case.

When I was in private practice and I brought a patient into the hospital I insisted on doing everything myself. I was then told by my superior that the purpose of a teaching hospital was to teach. A pathologist can demonstrate by letting a pupil see through the extra eyepiece in a microscope. A heart can be listened to by several students using multiple earpieces with one bell. But surgery can be learned only by the man actually doing it.

So should a patient worry that "his" doctor is not doing it all?

The old man let me do more and more, and sometimes he would come in late and by the time he was scrubbed and gowned I would have the abdomen opened, everything in readiness, and he would look and say go ahead and maybe he had done nothing but assist. Was it his case, had he done it? Yes. Because there was no mistake I could have made that he could not anticipate, no error that he would not have made me do over. Now I was the old man. And residents had to learn.

148

When a patient asks if I am going to do the entire operation I say yes, me and my assistants.

A patient says, I know everybody has to learn, Doctor, but not on me.

There are mechanical aspects to each operation, and they can be easily delegated. Anyone can do the clamp part of an appendectomy. The trick is to find the diseased appendix and hold it up for removal. It's putting it on the platter that's difficult.

So, yes, there are doctors other than "your" doctor taking out pieces of you and sewing things together, even though you have only one surgeon.

So I told Spector to do it again. He cut out the sutures along the side and put in the new row in a straight line.

As he worked I said to Newman, "Consider the type of stitches Paul is using. Why the U type?"

"Beats me," Newman said.

"He could be using a simple interrupted stitch," I said, "which is equivalent to putting your arm around somebody's shoulder. That would work. But this U stitch Paul's using is like embracing somebody with both arms. It holds a lot better."

If one is to work in a teaching hospital there are professional obligations to the institution. It isn't a matter of personal preference. If you didn't give part of your cases away after a while you would be told you were no good to the hospital. When a resident leaves to go into practice for himself he carries with him the silent endorsement of the hospital in which he has trained. And that means the attributes of the people who have trained him.

I accept all of that. It wasn't easy in the beginning because I had the same reservations as the patient exposed to interns hungry for experience. But the reservations were equally about my own ability to retain complete control. Now I accept the responsibility, and permit residents to do parts of some of my cases, with the complete confidence that the patient has been treated well.

Having said that, there are still cases that I will do completely only by myself. Especially difficult ones, for example. All secondary cases, those in which the first intervention had not provided a satisfactory result. And operations on nurses, and doctors, and nurses' and doctors' families. Because there are still intramural areas of primary allegiance. This is a tradition within the hospital and we see it as no contradiction.

149

I don't know if it is or not.

Why had the clamp on one side of Padget's jejunum slipped out of position? Because doctors learn the whole first and then the details. I thought about this as I watched Mrs. Rodriguez thread a needle. Most sutures are prefixed in the needle; this needle was unusually shaped and needed to be threaded in the old-fashioned way. I watched how she did it. First she fixed her elbows to her side. Then she put her wrists together. And then with all this bracing the thread went in easily. Tailors know this. Most people who use needle and thread do not know it. Nurses learn details without learning the reasons. Doctors learn reasons.

Patients seek out surgeons who are very busy because, being the best, being busy follows. "I went to this doctor for my heart operation because he's the most sought after, he does fifteen of these operations a day." No doctor, alone, can do fifteen operations a day. Maybe he gets to put in a suture or two. Yet they're all his cases because he assumes the responsibility for what, when, and where. It's just that he needn't cross all the *t's* and dot all the *i's*. It's better, perhaps, that patients prefer to be naïve.

"So, Newman," I said, "Have you decided to be a surgeon?"

"I don't think so," he said.

I could have felt rejected.

Yet he would have been yet another learner. I would never have the advantage of working with peers. Always a student.

"Why not?" I said, not being averse to stupid questions. If he were to answer he would be telling me the story of his life.

"I haven't got the hands for it," he said.

"Neither did Billroth, nor Beethoven for that matter. You find surgeon's fingers only in pickpockets."

"I'm also not happy with deformity. I'm not happy with people who are incurable. You go ahead and operate on them just the same. I heard a patient on the service say that if he awakened after the operation with the same pain he would curse the doctor and kill himself."

I was watching Spector's stitches. This time he was doing it right.

"The competitiveness," Newman said. "I don't like that. I don't see surgeons as a generous, particularly intelligent, or compassionate group. Maybe they can't be. But I don't want to have to be associated with the need to be tangential to patients, and to be one of several crabs crawling over one another in the doctors' lounge.

"Besides which, the being of a surgeon requires a declaration of dependence. You are manipulated like a marionette. With strings tied to you by administrators and clerks, to get your patient into the hospital, by another doctor who sends you the patient, by anesthetists to keep him asleep, by a team at the O.R. table, and the whims and unrealistic expectations of sick people. You must answer the telephone. You're trapped in the system of referrals. There are just too many compromises required to get to be a busy surgeon. Maybe it's worthwhile to you. Not for me. I want to be free of such entanglements, to do something by myself. Have you read *Middlemarch?*"

"What else, then? General practice? Psychiatry?"

"Maybe community psychiatry of some kind, not the one-to-one probing of neurosis. Or maybe public health. I think I might like public health.

"I like tying knots. I did maybe twenty, and it was fun. But what do you feel after twenty thousand, a million?

"I know Kocher of Switzerland got the Nobel prize for the work, but I'd find doing six thousand goiter operations repetitive and monotonous. Besides which, surgeons seem to have the style of buying a ten-cent stamp, with the aura of laying the cornerstone of a cathedral. I don't have that style, and I don't want to develop it even if I could.

"I sense the kind of excitement Paul gets, fighting for a case, doing something for the first time, learning. But I don't—I'm not sure I want to work with really sick people. I'm not sure I want emergencies. But I do see the advantages of the quick results, the excitement of the hard work, and the comforting effect of the ritualism."

I thought of the miracles in surgery, all the endless satisfactions. Newman would be missing all that, but there was no point in being a salesman. In his clinical years the medical student is beginning to make up his own mind.

He felt the need further to explain himself. I had taken all this trouble with him. "There are things I like. The trio thing—chamber music. You and Spector and me working together, a gestalt, each playing the proper notes and creating something more than the contribution of each separately."

"Good boy," I said.

"But you take this patient's ulcer. We take out a part of his stomach. I would rather work to prevent it."

"That's worthwhile," I said.

There was all the rest of it that he wasn't going to tell me. His belief in the persona of the surgeon, although neither Spector nor I nor most of the men on the staff fitted it anyway. More George Rafts than Gary Coopers. Yet Newman could not see himself ever growing taller, or developing a flashing smile, or wearing a dinner jacket without looking like either a waiter or a hired magician. He had lived more in books and humility than in the marketplace. He couldn't purge the legend, nor ventilate his own doubts. He might have said these things to Cathy Forge, and found understanding, but the opportunity had been lost. The grade-school music teacher who had classified him as a listener had poisoned his self-image forever.

A surgeon was everything he was not.

22

Dr. Rongy died about nine months after renting office space to me. Within a few days after the newspaper obituary there were no further calls for him. He had been a prominent obstetrician and gynecologist for over fifty years. He had had a one-to-one relationship with thousands of patients. Now I wondered how many of them would even remember his name. It was a sobering and depressing feeling to know that you could be forgotten so soon, no matter how many people you had made better. An artist signs his name to his paintings; a surgeon's scar is anonymous after a while.

Rongy's legacy to me was his office and Mrs. Smith. She became office nurse, bill collector, and friend—all office things except the all-night ear on the telephone.

For that I needed an answering service. I developed a close, almost personal relationship with a voice that came to know a great many things about me and my professional and social habits, but she never became more to me than a voice. This voice knew where to find me at any hour of the day and night, she knew my bachelor ways, then my wife and then my children; she knew when I would be in the library, and which stacks in the library, and where I might be having lunch and in which friend's home or wind concert I might be found. I have had a twenty-year contact with the same voice and never saw its face.

Mrs. Ellen Smith came as a young girl from Sweden after World War I. She had been trained as a practical nurse. For a while she tried to make a living in America in music, but there were few opportunities for a female cellist, and she met Dr. Rongy, who convinced her that her talents as a nurse were much more important. Rongy had maintained an apartment behind the office as his own

153

living quarters, and when he moved for privacy's sake, Mrs. Smith and her husband took it over for convenience. She worked for me two days a week and the rest of the time for the urologist and internist who shared the office with me. She was a stern woman, but with warmth and sympathy for the patients. On her desk she kept a plaque with the reminder: He jests at wounds who has never felt the pain.

I held office hours from four to six on Tuesdays and Fridays. Most of the time I was late, and I was there often until eight or nine. She made appointments at either ten minutes after four or ten minutes after five. That sounded as if patients would not have to wait. Sometimes, if a patient came at four, and didn't get to see me until six, and rightfully complained, I would explain that he had to wait because I would not curtail what I felt to be the necessary time I needed for a prior patient, and he was entitled to and would get the same consideration and if necessary the patient after him would have to wait, but I was running a practice to take care of people; I did not operate on a train schedule. Mostly they accepted that attitude and were happy with it.

Mrs. Smith taught me much about office practice. Her long experience with Rongy had alerted her to the female neurotic; to the sick shy elderly lady full of denial of illness; to the simulated concern of only curious friends, and especially to the rare malingerer and potential litigant. She had sensitivity as well as a sharp eye and an ear alert to relevant asides.

If I examined a female patient she was always there. Often if they were elderly and encumbered with corsets they would take forever to get disrobed, and I did not get to see them until they were properly draped and the area for examination discreetly presented. That was when I saw the need for an additional examination room. I could tell a man to drop his pants while I examined his hernia while in the other room the woman was just beginning to struggle with a girdle. Times have changed. Women get undressed faster than men. I like the way the ophthalmologist functions—all he has to do is to tell his patient to take off his hat.

I chose Tuesday and Friday because Tuesday was the first free day of the week—Monday was crowded with the detritus of the weekend. Friday was the best day of the week. I liked to go out on Friday nights. If I had a date I had the girl meet me at the office and

154

from there we could easily get downtown. In all of the years Mrs. Smith never referred to me except as Doctor. She was not, however, above delivering an opinion about a Friday-evening female that I took out for the second time. Somebody had to defend the naïve bachelor, was the way she explained it.

The office was at Seventy-first Street and Central Park West. Park Avenue, Fifth, and the west side of Central Park were where the specialists maintained offices. If Park Avenue was Harley Street, Central Park West was Wimpole. It wasn't fashionable enough for the lady who said the only time she went to the West Side was to get on a ship.

In those days I could park on the street and we kept the office doors open; a patient just walked in. No doctor would dare do that today. This was in the fifties and sixties. We didn't know, then, that those were better years to live and work in New York City. I liked the location because I could walk downtown to the theaters and concert halls, or I could take a bus. It never occurred to me to take a taxi. I was unmarried, beginning to earn money, but taxis were for the rich. Today I see an intern getting into a taxi and I think of all that I have missed.

I wasn't busy for a long time. The office with its paneling and rugs and judge's chair from which I could look sympathetically over to the ailing patient were things I had yet to grow into. Patients in the beginning were few. It is not enough for a surgeon to put out a shingle. Patients had to be sent by other doctors, and I began to learn something about the real world. Doctors were just as much interested in money as anyone else. Today the idea is current that they are even more interested in money than anyone else. I do not dispute that, even as I feel the wrench of paying the bills from the plumber, the electrician, and the tax assessors.

One evening at home I received a phone call from a Dr. Rand, a general practitioner I knew by little more than sight from the hospital. He had a boy with suspected appendicitis and would I be willing to meet him at the patient's home for a consultation. Of course I said I would. Today we don't go to the home. In a case like that I would now ask to have the boy brought to the hospital. I would call a resident and have him arrange for blood tests and abdominal X rays, all of which would be ready when I got there. It's a question of the changing position of the hospital emergency room. At one time it was used for accidents, traumatic emergencies. Now it serves as family physician and diagnostic center. Patients in need go directly to the emergency room.

But we all made house calls then, even the "frock coats" in chauffeured limousines. I found the boy presenting with abdominal tenderness and vomiting. I went out to the hall, where Rand and I discussed my findings, which were the same as his, and we went back to talk to the mother and father and grandmother, all anxious and worried. Rand said the boy ought to be operated on, and Dr. Schein was the surgeon of choice.

"He looks so young," the mother said, looking at me apologetically.

Rand convinced the family that despite my apparent youth I was very competent and they had to take his word for it. We took the boy in and I operated and everything went well. Afterward I discussed my fee with Rand.

"What do you usually charge?"

"Two hundred and fifty."

"All right, then," he said.

So I sent the bill to the family and they paid it. Then I got a call from Rand's nurse. "Dr. Schein, you didn't send a copy of your report."

"I thought I did." I said.

There was a silence on her end, and then she said something I didn't catch and hung up.

I was beginning to feel that I was missing something. I never got another referral from Dr. Rand. In the hospital patients carry name tags showing the lines of referral. These tags are also on display at the nurses' station. I began to see cases marked Pike/Rand. The case I had done was marked Schein/Rand. Pike was a senior surgeon at the hospital whose work I was never happy about. It looked as if my practice was always getting started and suddenly stopping.

One day, weeks later, I met Rand in the corridor.

"How's everything, Schein?"

"Fine," I lied.

"I wonder if I can tell you something—you're just starting out and I've been in this business for a long time."

"I'm always willing to learn," I said.

"Remember that case, the kid with the appendix? You got paid for it, right?"

"Yes—"

"So did I. You know what my fee was?"

"What?"

"Ten dollars. For the house call."

"I see."

"Your fee was two hundred and fifty dollars."

"I discussed that with you. You agreed it was a fair fee."

"And so it was. I spent a couple of hours with the patient. I took the time to reassure the parents. Then, if you remember, I told them I recommended you, I used their confidence in me to make them willing to use you."

"I know. I appreciate that."

"You do? Do you also appreciate the fact that I spent at least as much time with the patient as you and I got a fee of ten dollars and you got two hundred and fifty? Do you think that's fair?"

"It doesn't sound fair, of course not. Why couldn't you send them a bill commensurate with your services?"

"You can't do anything like that in private practice. I'm their family physician, I get ten dollars for a house call. They'd be outraged if I charged them any more."

"I don't understand—"

"Don't you?" he said.

I was innocent but hardly stupid. I knew that some surgeons showed their appreciation to referring physicians in tangible ways. In nontaxable cash disbursements.

I wouldn't split fees. There were several reasons. One was that it was illegal, and the other had to do with professional pride. If I was good then doctors ought to feel secure enough to send patients to me for surgery.

Rand didn't talk to me anymore about it, and I never got another referral from him. I was disturbed, and I talked to some of the older men. I learned about the medical marketplace. The splitters gave up 40 to 50 percent of their fees to the referring doctor, or they didn't get the patients. Pike was one of the busiest surgeons on the staff. I was one of the least busy.

Once I was called in to a private hospital to do a bronchoscopy. There were few surgeons doing the procedure then. When I was finished the doctor who had called me reached into his pocket and handed me seventy-four dollars and four quarters.

"What's this?" I said.

"That's your half of the fee."

"Half? A hundred and fifty dollars is the standard fee for the procedure."

"Well, sure. I got you the patient, didn't I?'"

I told him to keep it all.

"You're a kid," he said. "When are you ever going to learn?"

I still haven't learned. Fee splitting encourages poor surgery, or at least encourages poor surgeons to become rich. The patient ought to know what he's paying for. But mainly I am against it because it demeans. It seemed an easily soluble matter. The participating referring doctor ought to be paid adequately for his part in the case. He ought not to underestimate his role and ought not to be undervalued. The surgeon ought to charge less. It should be an open book. It's again a matter of both blades of the scissors. The problem then remains only where the wolf is a pig.

Being noble was made easier when I encountered an old college friend who had gone into private practice back in his old neighborhood. In short time his practice was more than he could handle, as if everybody had been waiting for the local boy to come back and be his doctor. He was glad to renew our friendship, and he began to send me cases. He was so busy he didn't have to think of adding to his income by arrangements. He was grateful for my just taking the surgical problems off his hands.

Also, I was being asked to assist some of the men working in proprietary hospitals. I was loath to go to them at first. By reputation they were pus pockets, dirty, poorly run. I found that, in the ones I went to, the opposite was true. Established by doctors for their own profit, they were also a means to escape bothersome administrators. The operating rooms were first rate, because this is where the money came from. The nursing care was excellent. If they lacked the armamentarium, the machinery for the unusual, at the same time they avoided complicated cases. There was a man I knew there who did five or six cases every day. Always the same four or five operations. He did them over and over and was superb at it.

I once asked Dr. Peters, "What do you do about complications?" It's always in the postoperative course that troubles come.

He looked at me as if I were questioning the cleanliness of his fingernails. "What complications? I don't have any."

I didn't believe him, of course. Then, after seeing him work several times, I realized that he was probably honest. No hematomas, because he didn't have to let the learner learn. No wound disruptions, because he closed the incisions himself, all layers by himself in the way he had found worked. No postoperative bleeding, because he was careful and experienced, and he couldn't shift responsibility.

The problem was that his hospital had become an intellectual desert. There was no one to share the excitement in technical virtuosity, no stimulus to maintaining diagnostic accuracy, no one to appreciate the smoothness of the postoperative course, because it was expected.

The hospital was also used by a prepaid medical group for which I was one of the surgeons. I operated there every Wednesday morning for many years. Always with the same associate surgeon. We assisted each other, peer operating. We got more done between eight in the morning and one in the afternoon than a teaching institution does in a day and a half. It was organized for efficiency rather than scholarship. Not all bad. It was compact, I wasn't competing. It was the same salary no matter how much or how little I did. Dr. Peters owned the hospital, our group filled his beds. He tolerated us as long as that was required. Later he asked the group to go elsewhere. While it lasted it was small-town practice in the city. I liked it. But I still wanted to be a professor, to get into the academic world where it was all scholarship, learning, the isolation of laboratories, and the tranquillity of libraries and professional meetings.

23

This is where we were in Padget's operation: neatly surrounded by four green towels blocking off the rest of him, mobilized out of the abdominal cavity and resting on his abdominal wall was the end of his stomach, clamped and held by Newman, and the loop of bowel, the jejunum, clamped and approximated in position. What we were about to do was create and then join the two mouths so the contents of the stomach would then go directly into the jejunum, bypassing the duodenum, which was now cuffed and forever closed off.

It was, according to Newman, looking down at the restricted field, like an illustration in a textbook. I said if it wasn't then we had done something wrong.

The stomach was already open and clamped. Spector made the matching opening in the bowel. Because the clamps lightly tourniqueted the jejunum below the site of incision there was no bleeding. The rubber-shod clamps held the vessels just tightly enough to prevent the small arteries from pumping blood to the area. We were working in a dry field. Technically, Spector was doing the procedure. Actually, since I was following him by holding the suture and making the loop all he was doing was the mechanical act of sewing in the area I was defining for him. Again, who does the actual operation? Answer: More than one person.

The open mouths were being joined by an over-and-over stitch which went back through the loops for a lockstitch. These sutures were going to be absorbed after healing took place.

"What we're doing now," I said, "is preventing complications later. That means a good bite, a tight lock, and no leaks at the corners. So start at the middle and work around. Neatness counts. As the lady said to me when she followed her husband on the cart to

160

the operating room, 'To you, Doctor, he's just a gallbladder, but remember please, he's my husband.' "

Newman said, "People used to die from this disease before doctors learned to do this operation. You could get religious, thinking about that."

I said, "Paré said he just did the mechanics; God did the healing. Paré was a religious man."

"I'm not a religious man," Spector said, using the forceps and needle with increasing skill and precision. "It was God's will to let perforated ulcers kill people. Why should he get credit for what we have learned?"

"There's a story," I said, opening the loops and holding them for Spector to come through, "about the farmer who buys a rocky piece of land in Vermont that hadn't grown anything before. After long and arduous work he developed an arable area and things began to grow. He was visited by a parson who said wasn't God's way marvelous, look how he created this miracle. The farmer said, 'That may be, Parson, but you should have seen this piece of land when the Lord had it all to himself.' "

"You're really whipping those sutures in, Paul," Newman said, half enviously.

"He certainly is," I said. "He is the product of the training by me and the fellows who have been doing this operation since the 1930s. They laid out, after making all their mistakes, exactly how it ought to be done for optimum results. As Bach said about playing the organ, it's a simple matter of hitting each right note at the right time. But the thing to remember, Spector, is that Padget will never know what we do here except that, if we do it well, he will no longer experience pain and discomfort when he eats. Always remember this is a patient and not an exercise. When you've been a patient yourself, as I have, you'll understand that."

"Doctors make lousy patients," Spector said.

"Doctors," I said, "have more postoperative difficulties than any other patient. No matter how well the operation is planned doctors seem to get the bizarre and unusual complications. The answer for the doctor needing hospitalization, as it was told to me, is to sign himself into another hospital under an alias."

"Is that a fact?" Newman said.

"Sure," I said. "Not only do doctors as patients get everything that can possibly happen, but it occurs despite the best-laid plans to avoid these problems. Doctors who know about this feel it's a kind of metaphysical revenge by *pro bonum publico* furies. But enough of that. Should a doctor know what it's like to be a patient? I think so."

"Why should I think of Padget as a patient rather than as this particular presentation of a surgical problem?" Spector said.

"Because," I said, "that's the difference between cutting a piece of meat and doing an operation."

"I don't know if I understand that," Spector said.

"Well," I said, "let me tell you about my hospital experience. I had a pain in my back, lower back. I signed in, because it hurt enough so that I couldn't work. It could have been anything from the popular disc problem to whatever you happened to read that day in the index to *Differential Diagnosis*. I had never been a surgical patient before—everything was new. You'd be amazed at what I learned about doctors, patients, and hospitals."

"What?" Newman said. I had noticed Newman was always more interested in the philosophy of medicine than its practical application.

"First," I said, "although you walk in, they immediately put you in a wheelchair. Then they take away your clothes, including your shoes, and put you in a nondescript white gown. Now you can do nothing for yourself although you're only a few moments away from the professionally dressed and functioning fellow who commanded.

"And although, as a doctor on the staff of this hospital, they give you a private room, the nurse who comes on at three-thirty in the afternoon has probably never heard of you and the nurse who comes on at midnight has certainly never heard of you. Then they give you medicine. The hour before you have been prescribing medicines for your own patients. Now as a patient yourself, you are not only not permitted to prescribe for yourself but they won't even let you know what medicine they're giving you. As a matter of fact a nurse almost clobbered me because she had a syringe ready with five milliliters of a concoction when only one milliliter had been prescribed, and were it not for the fortuitous intervention of the resident who happened to be there at the time the nurse would have injected the error. She wouldn't tell me what she was doing—I was just the patient."

162

"So you learned something," Newman said. "Now you know what patients are about when they complain and the doctor doesn't listen."

"Much more than that," I said. "I learned that the effect of the hospital is to so erase one's individuality that we're all alike—a disease with room numbers, without professions or I.Q.s or special talents."

As Spector was finishing up I warmed up to the subject. I had then shared the patient's experiences.

"You know how long it is between the nurse's last visit at ten o'clock and six in the morning? You think it's just one more night? You know what it's like to feel every crease in the sheet, hear every whisper in the air?"

"Didn't they give you a sleeping pill?" Newman said. "You've certainly prescribed sleeping pills for your own patients."

"Sure. But not for me. I hate medication of any sort. Was I afraid of barbiturates because of the danger of addiction? Surgeons are prone to things like that. The famous Halsted of Hopkins was an addict. Look at all the doctors on methadone long before it was decided to try it on heroin addicts. I don't take aspirins if I can avoid it. I don't like drugs. So there you are in the hospital and a nurse is handing you pills and standing around to make sure you take them.

"Then they take you in a wheelchair to X ray. Up to now you've been in a private room and nobody knows you're sick. Now you're exposed. The doctor is ill. How can that be? What happened to his own preventive medicine? Where's the father image? Where's sainthood? Can a priest be caught in a whorehouse?"

"And also he's not available," Newman said. "A doctor has to be always available in case his patients need him."

"Right. Now—if a little knowledge is a dangerous condition what about a specialist with a lot of knowledge? I came in with a pain in my lower back. What could cause a thing like that? The pain radiated down the back of my legs and I felt very weak. There were three things I thought of as most likely. Could I have a slipped disc? Some form of neuritis? Or a tumor? Since most of my professional life deals with tumors, I made a differential diagnosis in my own mind. I didn't think it was a disc because I had had no antecedent trauma, and discs usually produce symptoms in one leg, and mine

163

were on both sides. I was frightened by the thought of a tumor, but a tumor in this area, involving both legs, should have produced incontinence and gratefully I didn't have any. But why neuritis? I hadn't been exposed to nerve poisons and my diet was adequate. I was running a low-grade fever and that suggested an infection. Mostly I was afraid it might be one of the degenerative diseases of the nervous system. It wasn't typical, they usually didn't come on this way, but it has to start sometime."

"What doctor did you use?" Spector said.

"I went to a friend of mine, an internist, because I liked his nonalarmist approach. He brought in a neurologist who brought in another one because he wanted his responsibility diffused. You know a neurologist carries his own office with him. He carries an ophthalmoscope for the eye grounds and to look at the optic nerve, a set of pins to evaluate sensation, a tuning fork for the vibratory sense in the spinal column, and who ever thought of evaluating a vibratory sense in the first place? You ought to look that up, Newman."

"I've been trying to figure out what you had, Dr. Schein," Newman said. "Had you been in the Far East?"

"No, why?"

"You're beginning to sound like a character in an Agatha Christie novel."

"Don't think I didn't feel like a character in a book—not Christie, but something by Kafka or Chekhov, where the character is more than one-sided. Remember, along with the experts I was considering my own diagnosis. So they took a very detailed history, my two neurologists, and then after other tests, like the test tubes with the hot and cold water to evaluate heat pathways in the spinal cord, and after all the cranial nerves and all the reflexes and the position of my toes and all the coordination tests—that's when I really got scared when I found out my coordination had gone—when they were all done I did what every patient does: I said, 'So? What is it?'

" 'We think you have neuritis.'

" 'That's a lot of crap. Talk to me like a doctor.'

" 'That's what it is. What else do you want to call it?'

" 'That doesn't mean anything.'

" 'There's a decreased function of the nerves to the legs.'

" 'What's it due to?'

" 'We don't know.'

" 'Could it be a tumor?'

" 'Now you're talking like a surgeon.'

" 'Could it?'

" 'There's no indication, but we may have to do a spinal tap—'

" 'How long am I going to be laid up?'

" 'We'll know that in a couple of days.'

" 'How are you going to treat me? What treatment is there?'

" 'In neurology when we don't know what to do we give Vitamin B1. You fellows put a bandage on. It's the same thing.'

" 'Tell me something definite.'

" 'We have to wait for the results of the blood tests. We'll be in to see you tomorrow.' "

What they were telling me was exactly what I told my own patients when I did not want to tell them that I didn't yet know what the problem was.

I had decided upon signing myself into the hospital that I would not use bedpans. So I got out of bed to go to the john and that's when I was really frightened. I reeled like a drunken sailor. This was the first indication to me I had something that could be a serious problem.

The next day the first neurologist came in with a pack consisting of an aluminum tray covered with a heavy cloth. I used something like that for biopsies. I asked nervously what the hell did he think he was going to do.

"A spinal tap, Schein. That's routine."

Routine for me too. I had done hundreds. It's nothing.

"What about the postspinal headache?"

"We use a thin needle now. Besides you'll be in bed for at least the next six hours, so it shouldn't be much."

"What about—" And then I refused to reveal how scared I was. I had seen a patient become a paraplegic after the infusion of fluid for spinal anesthesia. I had seen cases of severe bleeding. I had seen a nerve hit and a permanent neuritis occurring as a result. But I had to assume this man was competent. He asked if I wanted to be held. I said no and got into the fetal position, arching my back.

He went off to have the cells counted and protein, suger, and glucose analyzed. The next morning I asked about the cell count and he said that part of the test had been lost.

I cursed him and the hospital but it didn't make any difference what I felt. I was a patient. That meant total passivity and total trust. The trust was based on lack of alternatives.

"I assume that there was no block and that he did the pressure studies right away?" Newman said.

"That's right."

"So you knew you didn't have a tumor."

"At that point it wasn't likely. Did that mean I stopped worrying? You know any test that's sure-fire positive?"

"And then what happened?" Newman said, like a child waiting for the rest of the story. Spector wasn't paying much attention. He never expected to be a patient himself, and it didn't have much to do with the anastomosis.

"Always have a curable surgical disease," I said to Newman, "like Padget here. Cut, clamp, and tie, and they get better, usually. Medical ailments go on forever."

"So what did you have?" Newman said.

"First let me tell you some more about being a patient. I became constipated, probably because the nerves going down my back also affected some of the nerves to the bowel. I had never been constipated in my life. I had always minimized constipation in my patients, telling them so often how natural it was considering their situation. But this was me and I found it distressing. And I had to ask for narcotics for pain. I almost never take medication, feeling reluctant to initiate dependency and concerned about secondary effects. And here I was asking for a narcotic because I was in pain. I was very unhappy. I was being forced to violate basic tenets."

"So what was it?" Newman said.

"I was there for three weeks. I was sick of the place. When the neurosurgeon came in I said he didn't have to bother; if I had anything that required neurosurgery it was no thanks because I didn't think their kind of surgery ever made anybody better. Then they wanted to do another spinal tap. They were after the spinal fluid cell count they had flubbed. I refused. I knew I was getting better. My coordination returned, my appetite became ravenous as the constipation disappeared, and I started to sleep. The leaves

166

outside looked green. I opened the window to let the wind in. I was restless and I couldn't stand the confinement. I longed for a wedge of pizza. I knew I was better. I signed myself out."

"But what was it?" Newman said.

"It got getter. All we finally had was a differential diagnosis."

"Probably a viral infection."

"Probably," I said. They never got the chance to do a second cell count.

24

I learned a fundamental yet startling lesson from my experience as a patient in a hospital—that none of us has any control over time. That plans for the future can be rudely and permanently terminated by the whim of circumstance. I had no religious conviction of preordination or the rewarding of the good and I had seen malice prosper. No one has control over his own medical destiny. No one can predetermine whether his tumor is going to be benign or malignant.

In that hospital bed I had time in which to speculate about which horrors were perfectly possible. I could have been paralyzed for life. I could have remained with chronic pain. I could have had a tumor resistant to any forms of treatment. I could have remained with the staggering gait which, unrelieved, would have forever prevented my functioning. I could have been prevented, by mere chance, from carrying out what I had spent my life preparing to do.

I decided then that one must not put off fulfilling his dreams for some distant unpressured period, and I made arrangements for a trip to Europe. I borrowed the money from my uncle. He not only thus expressed confidence in my professional future to the extent that he believed I would be able to repay him, but he also initiated the contact without which I could not have had the medical experiences I was looking for. He had operated on an influential Greek who, learning that his country was first on my list, arranged to have me met by a functionary in the Red Cross of Athens who could introduce me to the important Greek surgeons.

I secured plane tickets from a travel agent, packed one bag, and presented myself at the airport. It was a bewildering first time. I was a doctor, a surgeon. But I had never been on an international flight and outside of the operating room was incredibly naïve. Everyone else appeared to know exactly where to go, scurrying from ticket desk to numbered gates, following porters, confidently checking baggage, saying goodbye to friends. No one was seeing me off, but a telegram was delivered just before I left my apartment. From an old friend, it read: BE A BRIDE, RELAX AND ENJOY.

I was going to Germany, and so was an interested eavesdropper as one middle-aged German lady bade farewell to another middle-aged German lady. They embraced, exchanged words of caution, and the one left behind said, "Get a good coffee on the plane," and the other walked off without looking back.

I was also going to Italy, and I observed again two ladies saying goodbye, but in a flood of Italian that should have been orchestrated, rising and falling in pitch, a duet *a cappella* with no rests, and one went with the other to the gate and called a *con brio* coda after accompaniment was impossible. All of this heartened me and I wanted to tell those ladies that I, too, was on my way, and would be seeing their countries. I felt like Dick Whittington or young Ben Franklin or even Cortez. It was a moment of pure excitement never to be recaptured, like the first of anything, and I was almost glad of my illness for having motivated this.

On the plane I sat next to an elderly man and after a while we began to talk. He told me he was going back to Greece for a visit after having been away for most of his adult life.

"There's a time," he said, "when you have to take another look at your roots."

He was, he told me, a retired pensioned-off professor of philosophy at a small Midwestern college. I told him what I did. After a while I asked him how old he was. It was presumptuous, but you can ask things like this of people on planes, chance seatmates you are never going to see again.

"Eighty-three," he said.

People have so many different attitudes about their ages. He could have answered, "In my eighties," or "past seventy."

I said, "As a philosopher, and as a man who has reached the age you have, I would assume you've crystallized certain attitudes for yourself about being, living—and since I'm on my way toward Greece where all of these speculations were formulated, I wonder if you could tell me about them."

169

"You're a surgeon?"

"Yes."

"Could you, in a sentence, tell me the basic principle of your craft?"

"Yes. One should operate only when it's necessary, do what is required—nothing more or less—and do that without making any mistakes."

"I'll need more than a sentence for myself. The things I regret are not those I have done, but those things I left untried—the things I didn't feel, taste, or smell, the people I didn't get to know. Not enough time, too much fatigue, and reticence—those are the enemies. A few hours' less sleep, a few meals missed—how could that have hurt?"

"One more question," I said. "About this I am very curious. What books do you read now?"

"You mean now that I have to count the time remaining? I read only those books in which I already know the ending, so I can concentrate on the substance and style of the telling instead of on the plot. Viewpoints and the why of things become more important."

He fell asleep. I stared out the window and down at the islands beginning to be illuminated by the morning sun. I sensed their isolation from each other. Man needs man. Even animals in the laboratory kept apart from their own kind develop abnormal behavior patterns. Here the isolation came from poverty, which is the lack of alternatives. To do what my seatmate suggested as living well one needed the opportunity to move about. Which is what this trip of mine was for. In surgery one deals with books and relates to most patients only clinically.

Most people live and die within a two-hundred-mile radius of their homes. Fear says stay close to the store. There is a story of a shepherd on one of those islands who wanted to get away, to move about, he sold his flock and he bought a boat and filled it with olives and, taking his young son with him, sailed out to sell his produce to the neighboring islanders so he could talk to them and learn their views. On the way they encountered a storm. The boat overturned and the cargo was lost. The man and boy swam to shore, all their savings gone. After some months the son, looking out at the clear

170

inviting blue of the water, suggested to his father that they get another boat and try again. "What for?" said the man. "To prove once more that the sea is hungry for olives?"

I landed at five o'clock in the morning and a man came to meet me, giving his name and saying he was from the Red Cross, the cousin of the man whom my uncle had operated on in the United States. I was impressed. He took me to a hotel and the next day to the hospital and introduced the young professor from America to the Greek professor of surgery. I wasn't a professor at the time, but I saw the advantages of overlooking that inaccuracy. I was invited to the operating room.

I was interested in seeing the European treatment of ulcer cases. The professor operated himself from incision to closure. He did it all, tied every knot. His assistants held retractors and listened. They could never get to be professors themselves until the old man died or retired. The tradition was that the professor did it all. "That is the way it is in our country." The assistants did the scutwork. He had done, he said, over three thousand ulcer cases. I believed him. He operated with great deftness, and in the huge O.R., which handled three tables at once (our own operating rooms in the United States never have more than one table going in a room at a time), he went from one to the next. I noted that the ulcer disease did not seem far advanced, which it would have had to be to be treated surgically in America.

"True," he said. "There are medical reasons and social reasons governing our treatment here. This man leaves here and goes back to his island, goes back to a life in which he cannot be treated easily by doctors and medications and diet. So when we see the disease we treat it radically at once."

From Greece I went to Italy. A colleague of mine was practicing in a small town north of Venice. I had written him to expect me. On the way in a hired Fiat, I brushed at a bee determined to share transportation and in the scuffle I managed to overturn the car. I injured my arm, and the townspeople, having easily righted the light automobile, sent for my friend. He took me to the hospital of which he was chief of medicine. It was a political appointment; the countries of Europe practiced state medicine.

"What we do about surgery," he explained, "is treat people

conservatively and hope they do not need operations. If the cases have to be done I send them to the local surgeon, who is not very well trained. The big cases I try to get to one of the university hospitals. My surgical colleague used to get mad at me for doing that, but since I try to keep his mortality rate down he's come around to not noticing. I have too many sick people. I can't treat them all. I try to get to the sickest. The chances are that the people here have better cure rates than they had a hundred years ago, and we're all satisfied."

In the United States my friend had been the foreigner and consequently somewhat patronized. Here I was the foreigner. When we had lunch together I was impressed with a skill at using a knife and fork which I, at home, had never developed. He said he had a rich patient whom he was sending for an ulcer operation to Milan, and would I like to go along and meet the professor there.

In Milan, meeting the professor in his office, I was impressed with the walls covered with signed photographs of the medical luminaries of the world. I found out how he obtained them because when I left he asked that a photograph of mine be sent when I got home. Each medical visitor obviously received the same request.

At the operation he explained, "Our patients are very volatile, excitable people. This part of their nature, along with the economic stresses of our life, accounts for the considerable number of ulcer patients we get. What I do, therefore, is sever only those fibers of the vagus nerve which serve the acid-producing cells of the stomach. I do not do a total nerve severance as our Russian comrades have done."

"Does it work?" I asked.

"If it doesn't, we can always go back and do the operation according to the more radical methods. In our country the surgical pessimists emulate the Russians, and the optimists are learning acupuncture."

From there I went to Germany, to Tübingen. I did not have protective entrée, and introduced myself to one of the secretaries at the hospital who said they always welcomed colleagues from America and that one of them would contact me at my hotel. That evening I got a call from the professor ordinarius, who invited me to dinner. He picked me up at my hotel and apologized for not inviting me to his home because his wife had the flu. We sat at a

172

restaurant overlooking the Neckar River and discussed the operation I was to oversee the following day.

"You must remember," he said to me, "that we in Germany pioneered in gastric surgery. Our Billroth was the first man to take out the stomach successfully. We keep to his methods, by doing a gastrectomy for ulcer. I do it all; occasionally my first assistant, who has been with me for twenty years, gets to do one. You in America, with your residency system, your democratic way, cannot take the time to train your people in this kind of demanding work because you send your residents out into the community too soon. Therefore you can only do variations, instead of the complete procedure. And consequently we have a 98 percent cure rate while you have something less."

His point of view, his Teutonic solidity, was best expressed for me in the operating room, where the first thing to take my attention was a huge sign: *Nicht Sprechen.*

He wasn't all right, but he wasn't all wrong.

In England I went to the Royal Free Hospital in London. Just as the Channel separated the English by personality from their European neighbors so did it separate their surgical attitudes. Surgery there was closer to the American practice, in which treatment was geared more to the individual problems of the patient rather than to a blanket procedure for all. The origins of the ulcer, mechanical as well as personality factors, were taken into consideration and gastrectomies and vagotomies were done both radically and conservatively according to individual needs.

Observing the surgical treatment of ulcers was the thread which took me from country to country. Meanwhile I learned about restaurants—I found no bad ones in Italy or Vienna—toilets (Greece and Italy had some lavatories so appalling that constipation was preferable to taking even five minutes in that environment). I went to the museums, the bookstores, the parks, the concert halls. I let the wind take me and tried not to feel guilty about the lack of personal organization.

The night before I left Greece I went into a café and a woman seated at an adjoining table looked up at me and said hello. She was well dressed, pleasant-looking. I went to her and said, "Hello. Do I know you?"

"No," she said. "Does that matter?"

173

In some panic I made an excuse and left. I went back to my hotel wondering why I had behaved so maladroitly. I could have used some companionship. I thought of the old man on the plane. I was fifty years younger than he and already building up the series of regrets that his philosophy said was so damaging.

25

I came back from Europe with all the excitement, energy, and ambition which is the product of a stimulating earned vacation. I couldn't wait to go to work. I had seen the way the Europeans did it, and I wanted to borrow what was good and improve on what was inferior. For myself, my nonprofessional self, I felt that I had learned things of value. To one who had been essentially a learning machine I now saw the pleasure in amenities—how to use a fork in the left hand, how to listen to a dinner companion. I had always heard what people said, now I began to listen.

My practice—as if sensing that I was now ready—began to grow. I got referrals from doctors, and patients recommended other patients. I became family surgeon to the Pappas family, ever since the time I had gone to see the great-grandma living in that rarity in the Bronx, the house with garden, chickens, and two goats. After having removed her diseased gallbladder, I did her son's ulcer, and after that the grandson had appendicitis.

I loved my office. In those days one could go out on the streets in New York and breathe the fresh air and watch the lights across the park at night and walk reflectively around the corner to one's car that still had all its hubcaps.

Surgery changed, and I along with it. Trained as a chest surgeon, I found that most of that work at the hospital was channeled through two influential doctors, brothers, one a medical man who referred all his chest work to his surgeon brother. There wasn't much left over for me and, through necessity, as well as a growing interest, I moved down into the abdomen. Besides, there was less and less for a chest surgeon to do. Antibiotics had revolutionized the entire specialty. Where formerly one found lung infections and

175

the pulmonary tuberculosis that killed Keats and Robert Louis Stevenson and that initially had been treated by rest—which accounted for the sanatoria all over the world—we then treated the condition surgically by injecting air into the chest to collapse the lung, and these pneumothorax patients had to come back regularly to get their chests refilled with air. Later, we decided to collapse the lung permanently, and took out the upper three ribs along with portions of the fourth, fifth, and sixth—a deforming operation. When streptomycin came in, not only did it arrest the disease but it made it possible to remove the diseased area without the likelihood of infection spreading to the remaining healthy area. Now, with triple drug treatment, the disease is disappearing from the urban areas where it had once been termed the white plague. Surgery is no longer required.

The surgical complications following pneumonia, the empyemas, which had been recognized and treated by Hippocrates, and treated by stabbing into the chest and letting the pus out, were gone. Rarely seen anymore because of antibiotic therapy, this was reputed to have contributed to Caruso's death. Lung abscesses—so foul that the smell was distinctively unbearable (the story is told of the pretentious diagnostician on rounds pausing at the entrance to a ward, sniffing and stating, "There is a lung abscess in here," to be told by an assistant that the case was coming in the next day)—now a vanished disease because antibiotics in most instances abort the infection before it becomes an abscess.

Now most cases requring a pulmonary surgeon deal with cancer of the lung, a depressing and seldom cured condition, and I did not like to work in that atmosphere. I wanted to cure people. Besides, chest surgeons now were being displaced into the only field remaining for their talents, cardiac surgery. I found once more that here, as in Europe, operating-room doors have no knobs—one pushes or kicks his way into them, and I couldn't or wouldn't do that.

I was happy in the abdomen because a surgeon likes to see good results. You clear up an obstruction in the stomach and the plumbing begins to function. You take out an ulcer and the patient can eat lobster and pastrami sandwiches. You not only make people better but you can see the results quickly. Which may be part of

176

what the surgical personality needs. I could not find satisfaction in the long-term medical treatment of a diabetic with poor blood supply to the leg, or the atherosclerotic with high blood pressure who comes back year after year for treatment.

My office nurse, Mrs. Smith, began to be overworked, a condition that caused me obvious satisfaction as well as concern. It was time for a secretary. She came to me as a patient with an inflammatory disease of the bowel characterized by the infamous bloody flux, and obviously exacerbated by the throes of personal problems and the lack of employment opportunity in the field in which she had been trained. She was a very pleasant lady, brave in her adversity, very bright. I operated on her successfully and beforehand suggested that if the operation went well, which I had every reason to anticipate, I would put her on as my secretary if she were willing to secure the necessary skills. I operated, she went to school for a while, and I hired her. She was with me for thirteen years.

One night at the end of hours I got a call from a physician at the hospital who had sent me cases before; he had a patient with an obvious peritonitis and would I come up and look at her.

"Set it up, if you're sure what it is," I said. "Get in touch with my resident and I'll be there soon."

"It's not that kind of case, Clarence. It's special. You have to see it for yourself."

I didn't understand, but said I was on my way. If there had been doubt about the diagnosis he would have expressed it. But he was sure. The usual procedure to save time would have been promptly to prepare the patient for the operation. I was professionally curious. I drove up the West Side Drive with the good feeling of having had a productive day behind me, possibly an interesting case ahead, and the general well being I was experiencing because my practice was thriving.

I was met at the door by the attending doctor, who said, "Clarence, I'm going to take you to see something you probably haven't seen before. I won't try to describe it. You have to see it for yourself."

We went up to one of the rooms outside of which were two people, the man well dressed, in his forties, and, as I later found out, an accountant. His wife was his age, neat, lines of care in her face. They were both quiet and contained and the woman said, "I hope you will be able to do something for my daughter."

I thought of Alexander Pope. "A misshapen lump of malice and ill nature (four and a half feet tall) hunchbacked, victim of that long disease, my life."

On the bed was what I at first thought was an animal. Hair covered her entire body. In pain, from her lips came a soft whelp, as if from an injured dog. Her knees were bent close to her chin, the legs were atrophied, her feet looked like hoofs. She, or it, had obviously never talked or walked. The abdomen was grossly distended and it was evident there was a flagrant intra-abdominal infection. Something inside had perforated. It was a case of spreading peritonitis.

I went out to talk to the parents. I always had the task of talking to concerned relatives, but never before or since in this way.

"She's very sick," I said. "If we do nothing we can sedate her and in a little while she will just quietly slip away."

"But you can save her?" said the mother.

I didn't know what to say. What was in my province to say? How could I tell them that their daughter was a product of evolutionary arrest, that she could never be anything near a normal human being, something between a baboon and a dog. Nature had made a mistake. The curious thing was that this time it had survived.

"We would like you to operate, if you think you can save her life," the father said.

"I might be able to save her," I said. "But are you sure you want me to try?"

I didn't say what I wanted to say. Perhaps I wasn't entitled to make the judgment. I wanted to tell them that this was their opportunity to free themselves from a terrible burden, something surely that was ruining their life.

"We want you to operate," the mother said.

We took her to the operating room. She had twisted the intestine and it had blown out. I fixed it, and she made an uneventful recovery.

I had strong opinions of what should have been done, but I had to do what the family wanted me to. They tell of surgeons who, operating on colleagues with advanced incurable cancers, have tied off the ureters in order to ensure a quiet passing. There is a story of the man in Russia who is asked his opinion of his life there. "What do you mean? I read *Izvestia*—there are more apartments being built, the economy is strong, we have achieved great things in space—" "But what do you really think?" "What do you mean what I really think? I read *Red Star*—we're told our technology is a marvel in the rest of the world, our people rejoice in our system of government, our music and literature is the best in the world." "But what do you really think?" "I have my private opinion, but I don't really believe it."

Like the Russian, the surgeon has to be more than a realist.

It was time to write a book. I had done some thirty papers for the journals, but a book was necessary for several reasons. The most important was to establish myself as experienced in the field. Also, it was part of my European experience. They read books there, much more it seems than here, and the book lives while the articles yellow. It would be the results of my own work plus a compilation of the surgery on a structure only three and a half inches long and as wide as a pencil without whose function normal life is impossible—the common bile duct. About which nothing is common. A friend said, "About this little thing you're going to write a book? There isn't even a right and a left one."

Another reason for writing the book was that nothing quite like it had ever been done before in English. I secured the coauthorship of two radiologists, and after the text was written we needed illustration by a medical artist. I did not have the money for an experienced illustrator.

The problem was solved fortuitously by an operation in the same area. I was asked to see a woman with abdominal distress, and beforehand was given her history by the referring doctor. This was her second marriage; her current husband was a wealthy, educated businessman. Accustomed to securing the services of the best available in any field, he took her to see a man thirty years older than myself, a surgeon with a formidable reputation. He examined the lady, said she needed to have her gallbladder out. The wife refused him, she found his manner intolerable. She was a very delicate, sensitive woman, and the surgeon was gruff and unsympathetic. She went home and her condition improved slightly and then after a while she developed a fulminating cholangitis—an abscess in the gallbladder and bile duct. She ran a high fever, had

179

chills, and was jaundiced; further temporizing was out of the question.

The husband said, "Can you make her better?"

"I'm sure I can. Provided there are no further complications."

"Listen," he said, "you make my wife better and I'll do something for you."

Which was equivalent to the God bless you, Doctor, which is of no significance beyond the temporary glow of sainthood.

He left me in the hall and went back inside to see how his wife reacted to my examination and manner. He came out and said his wife had agreed to let me go ahead.

At operation I found a badly inflamed gallbladder packed with stones and one large stone blocking the bile duct. Using the optical instrument I had brought back from Germany, I looked into the duct to be sure no stones had been left behind—an incident not uncommon in this kind of surgery.

The husband insisted on having two nurses to watch over his wife. I told him that was unnecessary but he said nurses left the room to eat or take care of other necessities and he didn't want his wife alone for a moment. The night after the operation he called me at my home (having beat down the resistance of the nurse, who did not want to give him the unlisted number) and told me, "Do you know my wife is running a fever of a hundred and two and she's complaining of pain from the incision?"

"That's perfectly normal."

Fifteen minutes later he called me again. "She's restless and complaining about the tube in her nose."

"You have no business noting all these details. Since you can't relax I'll tell you what I'm going to do. I'll pick you up in fifteen minutes and you'll come home and have dinner with us. You can ask whatever questions you want, and at least I won't have to keep running to the phone."

I took him home with me for dinner for the next five nights.

On the ninth day I told him his wife was fine and he could take her home.

"Are you sure? We could stay longer if you're not sure."

I told him I was sure.

Then he made me an offer. Would I drop my practice and be his private surgeon? All I had to do was visit him and his wife each day

180

and examine them, just to see everything was fine. And he would pay me fifty percent more than I was making.

A doctor's dream. I refused.

On the morning he was to take his wife home he and I went across the street from the hospital into a little candy store, where he had a chocolate malted and I ordered an egg cream. Proving that neither one of us, the wealthy businessman nor the professional surgeon, had moved very far from his background.

"Now, about the fee," he said.

"Nothing," I said.

"What?" he said.

"I'm not going to charge you. No bill. However, I told you about that special instrument I used in the operation; nobody in this country yet uses it. That instrument is part of what is going to be written up in my book."

"What book?"

"The book I am writing about the bile duct, the part of the body that gave your wife her trouble. All I need to complete it is some money to pay the artist to make the illustrations."

"How much do you need?"

"Five thousand dollars."

He sent the check to the hospital. I thanked him, and he thanked me.

Finally, he said. "That wife of yours. Not only does she cook, but she's beautiful. Where did you meet a girl like that?"

A friend of mine had called me up at seven o'clock in the morning saying that a cousin of his, a student at Columbia, had been taken to a West Side hospital, where appendicitis had been diagnosed, and the surgeon there wanted to operate. What should he do?

"I don't know if she has appendicitis, and I never heard of the doctor who wants to do it, but if she does have appendicitis that pus pocket on the West Side is no place for anybody to be operated on, so bring her into the hospital. If she's very sick put her in an ambulance and if she's not send her up in a cab."

She didn't feel that sick, evidently, because she came in with a girl friend, looking for me. I came to see her in between cases and examined her. It was obvious that she did not have appendicitis, but a characteristic example of *Mittelschmerz,* the pain of ovulation

181

characteristic in many women. No surgery was required. I kept her for observation for forty-eight hours during which time a stream of interns, residents, and one of the radiologists thought it necessary to examine her. Each time I came to see her some male was sitting at the bedside. She went home, came to the office to see me for the one-time checkup; I sent her a bill, which she paid with a note of thanks.

Six months later we got married.

26

In a surgical career the first stage is the willingness to do anything for anyone, at any hour without concern about remuneration. In the second stage you want to work hard, do as much as possible, but you want to be paid. In the third stage you want to be paid but you don't want to do anything. From apprentice to master surgeon to consultant.

As in other branches of medicine and other branches of human activity, there are a number of knavish surgeons. Some are admirable in their disingenuity. I know a man who, after removing a perfectly normal organ, comes out to greet the family with a broad smile to assure them he found no trace of cancer. Another man I know has discovered the value of that exaggeration. He tells the family in advance of the surgery that the case appears almost hopelessly complicated, but he will do the best he can. If the case goes badly he points to his having given them the facts at the onset. If it goes well they kiss his hand for having overcome the difficulties with his superb skill. Either way he can't lose.

Surgeons are criticized for not having enough empathy with their patients, for not caring about them as people. I have never seen any evidence that patients are interested in their surgeons as people. They come to purchase a service. If the mechanic makes your car run better you pay his fee gladly without caring much about his personality. Young surgeons, being trained in hospitals, see the diseases, not the individual. In private practice I discovered this still to be the case, despite variations in the attractiveness of the people who came to see me. And if I remember them, I remember the case for its uniqueness, or because I had to do it at three o'clock in the morning, and less often because of an interest in the person himself. One can be less piquant than the disease that he harbors.

Weeping with your patients and for them is a guarantee of rapidly curtailing a surgical practice. After a couple of cases you can burn yourself out. A beautiful girl came in to see me with a melanoma of the shoulder. Subsequently I saw her on television modeling a cosmetic. In eight months she was dead. I came into the office in great irritability, I screamed at my nurse, I had difficulty in responding professionally to my next patient. My performance was impeded by sorrow and disappointment.

Some people, with their sweetness and acceptance of adversity, strengthen your belief in essential goodness, while at the same time affirming the illogic of who is to die and who is to live, who is to suffer and who goes unscathed. A kind act never goes unpunished. This old lady, who never weighed more than ninety pounds, was never well. She always brought me cakes, part of her European tradition. She was Czechoslovakian, met a medical student in Vienna, escaped Hitler, and came to America. Her husband was soft-spoken, cared about his own patients, sat drinking coffee with them, offered them the kind of *gemütlich* understanding that was as curative as was his medicine. He couldn't do much medically for his own wife. She suffered constantly from a variety of intestinal disorders.

When she came to see me her ulcerative colitis, which caused so much bloody diarrhea that she could not leave her house for very long periods, had been more or less successfully treated with steroids, which in turn had aggravated a duodenal ulcer. I operated on her for that ulcer and in the years that followed her colitis escaped the control of the steroids and she came back to me to do something about the misery of her life, essentially being tied to the toilet. We reached the decision that her only hope lay in being separated from her colon, which meant a ileostomy, that creation of an artificial anus on the side. A delicate, sensitive woman like this, instead of finding it intolerable, carried it very well, and was even grateful. Although she wore a bag all the time she was now free to go to the opera, a passion of hers that her former condition had made impossible. She made me a case cover for my clarinet, a beautifully sewn satin with my initials in gold brocade. Some time later she reentered the hospital, having committed some dietary indiscretion, and that night an intern was called by phone because she was restless. The intern, knowing nothing about her case, prescribed paraldehyde, a medication used to sedate psychotics and alcoholics. In a feeble elderly lady this prescription was a prime example of practice-by-telephone stupidity. The nurse, compounding the inanity, injected the drug far out in the buttock and pierced the sciatic nerve. Paraldehyde dissolved the nerve sheath. The patient instantly became permanently paralyzed in that leg.

She wore a brace and continued going to the opera. She came to see me and still brought me cakes. Her husband died, she lived alone for many years, and on a visit to her daughters in Connecticut she fell and broke her hip. Finally too many problems. She lost her courage, her interest in living.

I remember that lady.

I remember another old lady. She was ninety-two years old and needed a gallbladder operation. She found this invasion of her busy schedule a nuisance. Garden clubs, charitable organizations, knitting for her grandchildren. Women's lib yesterday. She discouraged visits from her grandchildren, she had no time to be a babysitter. I went to see her on the fifth day postoperatively. She was getting dressed.

"Hey!" I said. "What are you doing?"

"Leaving."

"What do you mean?"

"I refuse to eat this food any longer." She looked at me over her glasses. "You poor boy, are you forced to eat this food too?"

I thought the hospital food was pretty good, having learned as an intern to throw it down as rapidly as possible to bypass the taste buds.

"Dr. Schein, is there any absolute reason why I have to stay here?"

I would have wanted her to stay a few days longer; she was doing well and I preferred to get the sutures out while she was still in the hospital. Besides, at her age, I wanted to be very careful.

"Well?" she said. "You're not suggesting I'm not well enough to leave?"

"Leave," I said.

With that kind of energy staying any longer in the hospital was truly a waste of time, and she could come into the office for the suture removal.

I learned from her. I've seen people start dying at fifty from fear of aging.

I had a patient with an inoperable cancer. Afterward he said, "I've got a pretty bad disease, right, Doc?"

"We've got something to be concerned about," I said.

We didn't mention the word.

"Have you done everything for me you can?"

"Everything surgical," I said.

"I don't believe much in medicines, you know. I had a brother with a tumor, the medicines made him worse."

I couldn't answer that.

"Listen, Doc, would it be all right with you if I went to Lourdes?"

"Why not?" I said.

If he wanted to, if he believed in it, why not? And I know one thing about medicine, about illness. There are areas we don't know anything about. Cancers regress, people who are supposed to die keep on living.

A few weeks later I got a carton from Shannon with six Irish whiskey glasses with the note: "On my way, Doc."

I operated on a man of eighty-five who had cancer of the stomach. I expected him to live no more than eight months. Eight years later, with no trace of cancer, he came to see me with a diseased gallbladder. I took it out. I asked his daughter the other day how her father was. Ninety-three. She said, "He's driving me crazy. He complains of constipation."

"Didn't you suggest a cathartic?"

"Of course. His answer was, 'A thing like that could be habit-forming.'"

In private practice the condition most often seen was hernia. Followed by disease of the gallbladder, duodenal ulcer, and cancer of the intestine. Men talked about their hernias, women didn't. Especially older women, who were reticent to discuss anything so close to the genital areas, or to be examined. There are still doctors who examine such women without insisting they remove their clothes—resulting quite often in extremely puzzling diagnoses.

A girl of seventeen came into the office accompanied by a man apparently in his seventies. He needed hair, new teeth, and a

186

change of clothes. The girl said she was the patient, and I took her inside and she said, "What I want, Doctor, is that you make my breasts bigger."

I examined her. She had a marvelous figure. I said what she was suggesting was not only ridiculous but completely unnecessary. "Why do you want to do a thing like that?" I said.

She jerked her thumb in the direction of the waiting room where her elderly companion rested. "He likes them bigger."

The surgical decision in that case was easy. There were others not so obvious. A woman on whom I had operated for cancer of the breast twenty years ago and was quite well came to see me and introduced her seventeen-year-old niece. While the girl waited outside my old patient said, "Her mother, my sister, has died of cancer of the breast. I was one of the lucky ones. My mother died of breast cancer. What can we do with this child to see she doesn't get it?"

What, indeed? How much do we know? "Statistically," I said, "if you can get her to marry early, have children, breast-feed them, her chances are better than otherwise."

Should I have told her that the logical thing to do was amputate both breasts to make sure?

Pathology labs make mistakes. I removed a neck gland from a young man and the lab report was that it was a type of cancer. I told his brother; subsequently the patient was called for induction in the Army. His brother asked me to report on his condition to the draft board doctors. I sent in a letter saying that I had operated and found a lymphosarcoma. The young man was excused from the draft. After some years, seeing his family fairly regularly, and finding no progress in the disease, I asked that the slide be re-studied. It wasn't a cancer at all—it was a lymphadenitis—an infection. Happy ending. But what about the psychological trauma all those years?

During those years I began to collect out-of-print medical books for their historical and literary and artistic content. I was told about a Brooklyn bookstore on Henry Street run by an elderly gentleman who bought out the medical libraries of deceased physicians. I found his store, filled with musty volumes, a thin little man in a sweater in charge. After one or two visits we began to talk. He sold his books for a dollar or two and I said to him once, "How can you make a living from this sort of thing? You're lucky if you can pay your rent."

"Why do I do this? First, because I am interested in books like these. But before that, what should I do with my time? My wife is not well, and cranky besides, and she doesn't want me home for lunch. So I have this place, which to me is a cave, a place to escape, and I close for lunch and eat here, and there are people like you that come in and we talk. The fact that I will not get rich from it is not the issue."

I went to that bookstore for years. We always bargained. He would ask three dollars for a book and I would offer him two dollars and fifty cents. One day I was told if I wanted some books to rush down to Henry Street because the old man's sons were selling everything out for a dollar a book. Intruders to the shop had demanded his money and upon discovering that his total cash receipts were twenty-five dollars they had broken his neck and his arms and his legs.

There are no simple operations. Once I assisted a young doctor who was doing an appendectomy. The patient was a twelve-year-old boy. The surgeon applied a clamp poorly, the blood gushed forth, the patient needed a transfusion to replace the loss. As a result of the transfusion the boy developed hepatitis and as a result of the hepatitis the boy died. The surgeon is alive and well and successful and doing as poor surgery as always. We protect our own. If you get into medical school you will graduate and get your M.D. If you are accepted in a hospital for further training your peers will overlook your mistakes. Usually.

Another simple appendicitis operation: I went in to discover that it was not the appendix at all but congenital duplication of the intestine which had necrosed and required excision of part of the bowel. Not the sort of procedure an appendix-only surgeon would know how to handle.

I learned that many elderly people did not mind the sometimes two-hour wait in the waiting room. Even to letting others go in ahead of them. Some of those people had no other place to go, they liked sitting in the pleasant surroundings, talking to the other patients. Old people have a bad time in big cities. A grandmother told me she sometimes rode the subways, just for the activity, so as not to be alone.

Mostly I remember the satisfactions in private practice. Even getting up in the middle of the night, having the city to myself, the special quality of the hospital, the camaraderie of the night people. If the efficiency was down, the conviviality was up. More coffee was drunk.

I operated on a woman who had been a student of Pavlova. She came to this country, danced in various ballet companies, and was now semi-retired and teaching. She had gone to a surgeon before me and rejected him because she did not like the look of his hands.

My operation went well. Beforehand she made me promise that in the hospital she would not be forced to eat meat, she was a vegetarian, would have nothing to do with any sort of meat protein. I assured her that she would be getting fed intravenously anyway, with no animal content in the fluid. A day or so after the operation I went into my office to find the place crammed with flowers, at least a dozen bouquets. My nurse, Mrs. Smith, had no idea where they had come from. She called the florist, sure there had been a mistake, and was told that they had all been sent to Dr. Schein, without indication of the identity of the sender. The next day on rounds at the hospital I looked in on the ballet dancer, pronounced her fit and ready to leave. As I started out of the room she said, "Dr. Schein, you didn't like the flowers?"

Of course. When a ballerina performs well does she not receive bouquets on the stage?

27

I never doubted that my choice of medicine as a way of life was correct for me. But some doctors are happier than other doctors. I was beginning to find parts of private practice irritating. There was a question of feeding the feeders. You were, after all, at the mercy of referring doctors, else you didn't find yourself with many surgical cases. I didn't split fees, but it was necessary to split time, social engagements, back-rubbings of various kinds. If you didn't like a doctor and you were not able to conceal your dislike, chances were he was not going to send you his next hernia, or his next gallbladder. So you had to smile at people you didn't want to smile at. And when they decided that they did not like you, the method of putting you down, personally and professionally, could be devastating.

I had a patient who wanted me to operate on her because I had operated successfully on the patient in the next bed for the same ailment. The medical man who had hospitalized her said that if she elected to have me do it he would not be responsible. I cornered him later to find what, exactly, he would not be responsible for.

It was sometimes suggested to patients who had been referred to me by other patients that I was too young, and consequently not sufficiently experienced, or too old, and consequently not up on the latest methods. Or that I didn't operate on men, or on women, or that I no longer did surgery.

I had to leave the theater before the end of the last act to grab the phone in the lobby ahead of the other doctors rushing for the same thing. I always had a pocketful of dimes. Being called nights and weekends, which at first had been exciting and an indication of my importance, became increasingly annoying. My wife pointed out that the weekend, two days out of each week, when added up amounted to a hundred days a year, and what was worth a hundred days a year out of your life?

I had settled for seven days a week to do the one thing I wanted to do. But after a while, I discovered that there were other exciting things to do in life besides medicine. I read about Schliemann, a businessman, who memorized Homer and went out to discover the ruins of Troy. What, in his own choice of business, could have been as exciting? I wrote a letter to the University of Arizona, to their department of anthropology, which I had read was excavating Indian artifacts in the desert. I offered my service.

I got a phone call from a man at Columbia, to whom my letter had been referred. Would I have lunch with him? He wanted to know what strange breed of surgeon wanted to live in the desert for a couple of weeks. I convinced him that I was serious, that it sounded like a great idea, and, most important, I was willing to offer medical care in exchange for the opportunity to participate in dirt archeology.

They accepted me. I arranged to have my practice covered and I went to Tucson, from where I was picked up in a small plane and dumped in a cow pasture near Globe, Arizona. It was out of a cowboy movie. The dig was ninety miles away, on an Apache reservation.

I lived in a tent, dug along with the others, learned to take a shower with one splash for soap, another to remove the soap, the run-off water saved for washing clothes. I learned to drink warm gin and sang campfire songs. I held a daily clinic for the members of the expedition, and for the Indians on the reservation. Most of the Indians brought their children. I didn't know much about childhood diseases, but I could tell a sick child from a normal one. Luckily, most of the cases could be handled from my memory of the pediatric clerkship at Bellevue.

We made an exciting find. A kiva was uncovered with three intact skeletons and evidence that they had died in a fire. And inside one of the skulls was what looked like an intact brain, except that it was shrunken to a fourth the size. We encased it carefully in plaster and I later brought it back to the university for examination by neuropathologists who examined it and decided it was truly a brain. It had to be at least eight hundred years old. No definitive explanation was given for its preservation or its size.

I went back to work in the city. I did gallbladders and stomachs and hernias. I got paid for doing what I liked, but I grew increasingly dissatisfied with making it in private practice.

I was too much at the mercy of referring physicians, patients, and the inexorable passage of time. I needed time out of a routine.

I took a summer to throw off the incessant pressures, and convince myself that I was not intellectually withering. I took three courses at the University of Colorado, none relating to medicine. The first was in medieval German art. I learned names like Tilman Riemenschneider and Veit Stoss. I was fascinated with the pace of academia. I took a course in American political biography, and the literature of the Puritans. I wasn't there for credit, I was older than the other students, but I studied and took the exams for the fun of it. I came back to work refreshed, happy that my brain had not shrunken like the brain of that ancient Apache.

A woman came in with a strange trouble in her hand. It was white, she had difficulty in flexing it, and there was no easily ascertainable cause. After examination and X ray, I discovered that she suffered from a rare anomaly: she had an accessory cervical rib in the neck. Snakes have it. People are not supposed to have it. It pressed on a blood vessel, thrombosing it so there was decreased blood flow to the hand, and the fingers were becoming cadaveric.

Before proceeding to correct the problem, because of its rarity I discussed the case with a friend of mine who did the hospital photography. He wanted to do movies. He suggested that we do a movie of the case.

We took pictures of the hand, contrasting its strength with the other one, took temperature readings of the fingers and wrist and forearm. But who was going to pay for the project? I agreed to donate my services, so did the photographer, we got the hospital to grant a modest fee for the materials.

I operated, my friend ran his camera. After removing the rib and putting in an arterial graft the blood supply came back to the hand. It was never to be as good as the other one, but the patient regained power and appearance and, most important, was not faced with amputation.

We presented the film to a conference of the American College of Surgeons in San Francisco.

I wore a tuxedo. I was on stage before a full auditorium of the most prominent members of my profession. This exposure, plus my

192

book, and I began to receive offers. Virginia, North Dakota, and California. I didn't want to leave New York. Then, at my own hospital, the administration in surgery changed and the opportunity for full time in hospital practice presented. Was I interested in making a change from a fee for service practice to becoming a salaried employee?

My wife also said yes.

The change meant a substantial decrease in my income. In return I would be offered a chance to teach, do research, while continuing to operate. Supposedly I would have better control of my time. That illness had taught me that time was the only thing that couldn't be retrieved. This was an opportunity to buy it.

I couldn't make an immediate decision. I tried to balance one way of living against the other and everything seemed to cancel out. I needed a sign.

Meanwhile, something was happening to me as a doctor.

A student is fascinated by the opportunity to help people. Somewhere along the line, certainly by the time he becomes a resident, he becomes primarily interested in the disease. This carries through to private practice. You go through the motions of empathetic response, you see several members of the same family, you try to see patients as people. But mostly you're still looking at the disease. Diagnosis, procedure, prognosis, cure rate, follow-up. It becomes the gallbladder you did last week, not the operation you performed on Mrs. Carter. This attitude makes you efficient, and saves a lot of time so you can see more people and, incidentally, make more money.

Then there is a change, and often it comes from having children. A surgeon gets the smashed-up car, the possibilities are limited. Having a child of your own means attention to minutiae, concern about the trivia which you rudely dismiss in your own patients.

The pediatrician, called when my daughter had a hundred and three, saying "Stop worrying, Schein. And stop trying to diagnose. What do you know about kids? Most of their ailments are self-limiting. Most kids have what most kids have. Stop being a worried father."

Of course, I could not stop being a worried father, like all fathers, even if they are not surgeons.

I was becoming sensitized.

Then, as you get older, you begin to discover signs of your own mortality, and this carries over. Before you are an indestructible entity with a brain and a pair of hands that know what to do. You have traveled far from the common hypochondria of the medical student who sees symptoms in himself of each new disease he studies.

And medicine was changing. Only in America was the doctor permitted to practice according to his own wishes, in essence unsupervised, an antediluvian remnant of private enterprise. Every other country in the world utilizes the physician as a public resource. "How could we," said a doctor from another country, "place the health of our people under the caprices of doctors working alone?"

I was beginning to see minorities in my private work. Formerly the poor, the blacks and Puerto Ricans, formed the bulk of the patient load at the city hospitals. Now with medical insurance, they wanted the same individual attention that was formerly the province of the white middle class. And the hospitals were increasingly going into the business of medicine, not just being the workshops of the private practitioner.

Some form of socialized medicine was coming. To allay our fears of total capitulation it would be termed health insurance, but what it meant was that the doctor would be a civil-service employee, like everybody else, working for the state. And, since it was coming, ought I not get in early so that the inevitable would be more palatable?

But there was always an "on the other hand—"

Not being able to solve my problem with the traditional methods of logic on which I had based my behavior all my life, I left it to the primitive brain to make the decision. On a trip to Israel I discovered in myself the kind of symptom which alarms even the most medically uninformed. I was informed, and my face grew just as pale. One morning, at my postprandial bowel movement, I discovered that I had painlessly filled the bowl with blood. It happened three times.

Hemorrhoids, polyps, some benign ulcer of the colon—any of these might have caused it. I didn't believe it. I was convinced I had a bowel cancer.

I, not one of my patients.

194

I arranged for a barium enema, the test to determine whether there is any abnormal condition in the colon or rectum. I went to an unknown radiologist, in a strange hospital, in a foreign country. The radiologist turned out to be a tall, thin South African, who was kind and understanding, and I apologized in retrospect to all the patients to whom I might have seemed gruff and unsympathetic in their panic. He took me along each step in the procedure, giving me his findings. As I turned right and left at his signal, feeling the intra-abdominal distension from the barium, he said, "It's in the sigmoid colon now, normal redundancy, looks okay, scooting around the splenic flexure, no obstruction so far, now across the entire colon into the hepatic flexure, looks good so far. Filling the cecum, some of it refluxing into the small intestine. I'll take a few shots of this, but fluoroscopically it all looks good. I'll need a post evac film, so go in the john and get rid of the barium. After that we'll get a good view of the mucosa."

I went into the W.C. and as I sat there I heard outside the sounds of spring, with an underlying *swish* that I could not at first identify but then realized was the sound of a scythe being rhythmically drawn through tall grass. All the apocalyptic allusions to plague, disease, and death based on that ancient instrument poured through my head, and I made a covenant with myself. If it turned out not to be cancer I would regard it as a sign. I would give up private practice and take a job full time at the hospital.

I went back for the conclusion of the examination, and the radiologist said he found no abnormalities. "These examinations of normals are boring to do," he said, "but there is a certain pleasure in being able to reassure my patients."

"I understand what you mean," I said.

28

Spector was completing the anastomosis. He had already sutured the inner layers joining the mouths of what remained of Padget's stomach to the jejunum, the second part of Padget's small intestine. The stomach contents were now ready to move from the stomach, bypassing the former ulcer site in the duodenum.

Spector was now starting to suture the outer layer of the anastomosis. Newman said, "For the outer layers he's using silk; he used catgut inside. Why, Dr. Schein?"

I was sure he knew the answer, but he was giving me a chance to teach or to show that he detected the difference. That's why the medical student was there, and that was why Spector was there.

"Catgut," I said. "It comes from cats?"

"Sheep," he said.

"Right. It is absorbed by the body tissue. Silk, on the outside, isn't. It will stay there forever. Colored black—you think silk comes from the cocoon that color? Why black?"

"Why?"

"So it can be seen."

"Why the curved needle on a holder? Why not a straight needle like the tailor uses?"

"Mrs. Rodriguez," I said to the scrub nurse. "When is the last time you were asked for a straight intestinal needle?"

She thought for a moment. "Not since old Dr. Owen died. None of the new people use it."

"Thanks," I said, feeling twenty-five years of practice being peeled away. "The answer, Newman, lies in tradition. Tradition is something that makes you do something in a certain way because

196

that's the way it is done. Then you think of doing it another way and so start a revolt or a new tradition. The answer is a straight needle is just as good. Maybe better because you don't interpose an additional instrument, the needle holder, between you and the feel of the needle. When you get to do it, make up your mind. Whichever feels easier."

"What makes me sad," Spector said, "is that everything we do is eventually going to be superseded anyway. Instead of suturing by hand they'll eventually so improve on the stapling machine that we'll be using clips. Just as once we had to thread our own needles and now they're all prethreaded by machine. Everything is going to be medical or mechanical. I went into a field which is going to be obsolescent. Why didn't you warn me about this earlier, Dr. Schein?"

"Don't worry, you'll live out your lifetime doing it in this antiquated way. Even if medicine will cure all ulcers in the future and this operation of ours will be only an addendum to the text of pure historic interest, there will always be accidents requiring surgery and there will always be things for surgeons to do."

"Work makes us surgeons happy," Spector said, "and I resent these new kids bitching because they are asked to do the work they consider out of title. Bloods and urines are given over to technicians. You know what's happening? Doctors no longer know how to do a urinalysis, they can't do accurate blood counts, certainly they can't do a reliable differential count of the white cells. Lab technicians are now the only ones who can do blood sugars in the diabetic. We've turned the starting of infusions over to an I.V. team, and they also draw the bloods. Another group does all the passing of tubes. The respiratory care is now assumed by another group of technicians. How do you recognize a doctor anymore, because he signs the Medicare forms and the death certificates? I'm going out to practice medicine, and I want to be able to do these things. Is it so degrading to have to wheel a patient to the X-ray department?"

"Be calm, Spector. This new generation will win the battle and lose the profession," I said. "Operations have to be done in an atmosphere of calm. For example, Newman, you didn't know that doctors used to wear sweatbands on their foreheads—it was a part

197

of the O.R. garb. Then you remember all the medical movies, how the solicitous nurse wipes the forehead of the poor perspiring doctor. Rodriguez, when's the last time you patted me dry?"

"I don't go to those movies," Rodriguez said.

Spector said, not having been at all distracted by the byplay, and continuing to sew, "I know a story about Charlie Drew at Howard. Drew, the man who really started much of the routinization of the transfusion business, blood banks and so on, was in a ward and found an old lady lying incontinent in a mess of her own making. He picked her up in his arms, asked a nurse to clean up the bed, while he carried the patient to an adjoining area, where he cleaned her up and put on a new nightgown and brought her back. He didn't say it was out of title and that a doctor wasn't supposed to do things like that."

I looked over the screen to Patel, the anesthetist, "How are things on your end?"

"Normal," she said. "I haven't heard anything from you that there was anything wrong. Everything charts out all right. How much longer?"

"We just have to check out what we've done to the stomach, and then we'll take out his appendix and be ready to close. Let's reposition the nasogastric tube now."

It was coiled in Padget's stomach. I could feel it lying inside like a snake. Patel began to pull it through the nose and I felt the tube move and when it was straight I called to her to stop and she taped it in place on the bridge of his nose. This suctioning out of the stomach contents enables the motor power to return, something that would be delayed if the stomach pouch were distended.

"So, Newman," I said, "you watch and you learn. In the old days you used to watch but you didn't always learn. Surgeons, especially plastic surgeons, used to be not only prima donnas, they were also jealous of revealing their tricks. So sometimes at a special point in the procedure they would hunch over to conceal what they were doing. Of course, somebody like Halsted you could fall asleep watching. He used a different needle for each step in skin closure. Talk of regal prerogative—twenty needles for skin alone, and that's in the days before they were disposable. He disregarded the disadvantages of long exposure to the air. He believed there had to be the most delicate and complete control of bleeding to minimize hematomas. He wanted no bleeding at all. He closed off each capillary. Speed is good but not at the expense of trauma."

"Done," Spector said.

"Let's check it out." I said. "Let's be sure the area where we closed off the duodenum is secure. Rodriguez, give me a bulb syringe and a solution of Kanamycin." I took it with a kidney-shaped basin that fit against the abdomen and irrigated the area, aspirating, and diluting the possible contamination. I used about a liter of fluid, the aspirator sucking it up as I went along.

I looked at the site of the anastomosis and put my finger in to make sure no diaphragm had been created. I made sure there was no ooze from the site where earlier there had been some bleeding caused by the retractor. Spector had done well. "One final look," he said, "where we cut the vagus nerve."

"Check the spleen," I said. "Sometimes after a vagotomy there's some damage."

"All okay," Spector said.

"Newman," I said, "how much blood loss do you think there's been in this operation?"

"How would you measure that?" he said.

"Spector?" I said.

"Well, looking at the suction bottle, and checking the lap pads, I'd say about 200 cc. Of course for accuracy we could also weigh the pads before and after."

"It's amazing," Newman said.

"What's amazing?" I said.

"Here's a major abdominal operation and blood loss is only 200 cc. A man goes in and donates 500 cc to a blood bank and doesn't feel the loss."

"It's because we're calm," I said. "The enemy of any operation is anxiety. That's why we don't operate on members of our own family. That's why I hate a case from a referring physician who is excitable and transfers his own problems to the patient and to me, the guy who wants to know exactly what am I going to do and how and what if and so on. I don't want cases from someone like that. I'm compulsive enough for the two of us—me and the patient. Sometimes there's anxiety if you have an especially important patient, where his importance influences surgical decisions. Like a recent president who was given the safest procedure instead of one most likely to afford the best long-term results. You allow anxiety into the operating room and anything can happen. In any case you have to be prepared. Like the cross matching we did on Padget before we started so the blood bank had his blood sample, and could rush us whatever we needed if we had needed it."

"Talking of important people," Spector said. "We could have cured Napolean's ulcer. Not only that, if we had cured it early, his dyspeptic disposition might not have affected the world as it did. It's not mere whim that he always spoke of an army traveling on its stomach. Surgery in politics. Maybe there's a book there."

"O that mine enemy would write a book," I said. "How about Washington? He wouldn't have been bled to death had we been there."

"Gibbon," Newman said. "Had we been there he would not have written the *Decline and Fall* because his scrotal swelling kept him in a chair. Hydrocele or hernia is what he had."

"We might have been able to cure Marat's itching, which kept him in the bath and a target for Charlotte Corday," I said.

"De Maupassant's syphilis," Newman said. "We could have done something for him."

"Dean Swift," I said. "What about him?"

Newman didn't know. Spector didn't know.

"What do you think made him so cantankerous? He probably had Ménière's syndrome. His inner ear might have been treated by desensitization. But then he might not have written *Gulliver's Travels.*"

"Let's get on with the job. There's too much irrelevant talk."

"I don't know," Newman said. "There's no such thing as irrelevant. I've seen several operations now and it seems to me that surgery for the most part is doing the same old thing over and over."

"Nonsense," I said. "You think a musician always plays notes in exactly the same way?"

"But more than that, you work on an anesthetized patient. He doesn't know what's happening to him. He doesn't have a choice. I don't know if that's for me."

"What choice? Does he know what the alternatives are? Should he even be consulted? He comes in, says, Doctor, I'm sick, make me better. We make him better. What does he know about anastomosis

200

and shunts and excisions and nerve pathways? You know, Newman, you don't have the surgical personality."

"What is that?"

"Well, first of all, you don't have the excitement about the tools. You don't think it's a great argument whether it's the third or fourth finger that goes in the scissors. You don't even want to discuss which blade does the cutting. But more than that, you think the patient ought to participate in the decision. His option was to get the disease. We correct it, the patient adjusts. We accept the facts as they are, not as we would like them to be. You want to look at the total personality, we look at the problem. You're too emotional and that's being vulnerable and that impairs function. You see too many questions where we already have the answers."

"Anyway," Newman said, "I haven't decided. I wasn't told a surgeon had to be a pachyderm. Meanwhile I see Cathy Forge out there scrubbing up. This was to have been her assist, you know. I only came in because she was presenting a case at the conference. I've got a new patient to work up. I could stay if you want, but Cathy's ready to take over."

"Okay, Newman. Thanks for helping. As far as your eventual choice of specialty, you've got some time yet. If I haven't convinced you through precept that mine is the most glamorous, interesting, and ultimately useful branch of medicine, then the *culpa* has to be *mea*. I wouldn't do anything else."

"I've been very impressed," Newman said. "Honestly. And if I have a bum gallbladder or stomach I want to come to you, Dr. Schein. But I don't know if I have the skin for it."

201

29

Cathy Forge pushed through the door with her shoulder and came into the operating room with her scrubbed hands out before her looking oddly like a supplicant. Sometimes we September professors cast a fond eye on our May students. It wasn't difficult with Cathy. She was the traditional California blonde, assured, also very bright, it was nice to have her near. Newman did the operating room do-si-do with me, back to back, and went behind the nurses' table toward the door. He said to Cathy, "Dr. Schein let me do the gastrectomy. It went very well."

She said, "What!"

I said, "Newman, you start rumors like that I'll have you defrocked."

Cathy went to Mrs. Rodriguez, who had taken the gown out of the pack and was holding it up. The forty-year-old supervisor, at the top of her profession, dark-skinned and the product of her own admirable ambition, assisting the young fair girl on her way to becoming a doctor, each secure in the caste relationship of the O.R. No democracy here, and for that reason it worked well. From the porter to the orderly to the anesthetist to the resident to the surgeon, each knowing his place and performing to the best interest of all. I was the captain. I liked it that way. I was a liberal in most things, but no democrat here.

Cathy, gowned and gloved, came to the table, passed in front of me as I stepped back for her, positioned herself at my left, not enough room for her to face the table fully. I had stepped back because my back was not as sterile as my front. The front faces the table, faces the patient.

I said, "Observe. There's the remaining pouch of stomach, the duodenum closed off, the anastomosis completed. O.K.?"

"Neat. Very neat. Like the book."

"If it didn't look like the book we'd have to do it over."

"So what's left?"

"The appendix."

"What about it? He came in for his ulcer and that part's completed."

"We're going to take out his appendix."

"Why?" Cathy said.

Which showed how far we have come. There was a time when the surgeon in charge would have reacted violently to such a question from the student graciously permitted to observe the great man at work. Now we not only welcome the question but answer it in detail.

"Because," I said.

"Be serious, Dr. Schein."

"Okay. We're going to take out his appendix because it's there. Like Everest. It's healthy, it's pointing properly at three o'clock, we can take it out with practically no chance of a complication. And why should we do it? Because this is the third time this man, this patient of ours, has had the integrity of his abdomen violated surgically. We don't want it to be necessary again. He's still young enough to get appendicitis, and why should we not spare him that potential problem?"

"You can't just go in and do a thing like that, can you? I mean, what about informed consent?" The students know about things like that.

Had I discussed with Padget that I might consider taking out his appendix? I had not. We had talked about what I intended to do with his ulcer.

"Patel, you've got the chart there. Turn to the consent form. What do we have?"

Patel said, "He's signed consent for removal of part of the stomach and the ulcer, cutting of the vagus nerves, and such alternatives as might be required. No specific consent for the appendix."

"Who knows," Cathy said, "but what the appendix serves some function we don't know anything about?"

203

"Sure," Spector said. "There was an anatomist who thought that was where the worms were stored to keep them out of the rest of the bowel. Of course, that was in the seventeen hundreds."

"Coffee," I said. "I took an ulcer out of a patient and his wife asked me if it could have been caused by coffee. I said I didn't know. She said, then how did I know it wasn't caused by coffee?"

Cathy said, "If you remove a healthy organ without consent, just because you think it's a prophylactic procedure, what does that do to the legal aspect?"

"Screw the legal aspect," I said. "I am concerned here with the only thing that should concern any surgeon. The welfare of his patient. I can't do anything about his past, I have done something therapeutic concerning his present, and I intend to do something preventive about his future."

"I'll tell you about a case I saw when I was at the city hospital," Cathy said. "A storekeeper was shot in the abdomen during the course of a robbery. During his operation it was discovered that the bullet through some fluke had actually done him no real harm. The surgeon decided to take out the appendix so long as it was there. So what happened? The stump of the appendix blew—maybe the tie was insecure—part of the intestinal contents got into the abdomen, he got an infection which got into the bloodstream and he died of bacteremia. So the gunman now became a murderer. But who was responsible? The assailant gunman or the surgeon?"

"Come on, Cathy," Spector said. "All that's just anecdotal. If we surgeons are going to be tied down by a bunch of wild stories we couldn't do our job. Informed consent can mean anything. A patient rolls up his sleeve, that's consent to an injection. There was a case in North Carolina where the judge ruled that no surgeon ought to shrink from his medical duty for fear of a lawsuit."

"Fight, children," I said.

"Patients' rights are important," Cathy said. "We've come a long way from charitable immunity, where you could do anything you wanted to a patient in the city wards. Now a patient has to have everything carefully explained before an operation, and that's how it should be."

"Well," I said, "take Padget. Suppose I said to him the night before his operation that there was a 1/10-percent chance that he could die during this operation, from events beyond my control.

That there was a 2-percent chance that the closure might blow out and form an abscess. A 5-percent chance of dysfunction of the anastomosis. A 5-percent chance of developing significant adhesions. That none of this was predictable. That with the best technique possible it still might not be avoidable. Suppose I told all this to a man with his anxiety. All the uncertainty he had picked up from his psychiatrist would now be transferred to the surgeon who had been the father figure protecting the patient's welfare, and what kind of an alarmed character would we have on the table? What purpose all the calmative drugs we gave him beforehand?"

"Once," Spector said, "I explained all this beforehand to a patient and she went out the window. That's informed consent for you."

"A lawyer I know—" Cathy said.

"You know lawyers?" I said.

"The man I live with," Cathy said.

I felt a pang.

"He says that in common law the patient has to be protected from a negligent action. That a surgeon has to use reasonable judgment within the accepted practice in his community."

"Fie on him," I said. Living with him, I said to myself.

"Haven't we progressed from Babylonian medicine, where they cut off the surgeon's hand if the patient died? In China you could be buried along with your dead patient. True, in Augustus' reign if you did well they exempted you from paying taxes. In the rabbinic code they recognized the possibility of imperfect judgment, and doctors were not to be punished for well-intentioned but bad results because, they reasoned, who then would be a doctor?"

"Look at the doctors leaving practice because of the intolerable malpractice insurance rates," Spector said. "Should a doctor have to practice defensive medicine, instead of what his training suggests he do?"

"We have to respect the rights of the individual," Cathy said.

"Feminist crap," Spector said. "I always said women didn't belong in medicine. The thing to consider with this appendix is that it's there, nice and accessible, we don't have to enlarge the incision, it's a two-clamp procedure and that's that. Also, Dr. Schein was saying he might let you do part of it but I don't think you deserve it."

205

"Wait a minute," Cathy said. "You'll let me do it?"

"I say no," Spector said. "You're not even going into surgery. You want to be a school doctor or something."

"Hey," Cathy said, "I would like to do it."

"Not unless you can tell me something of the history of appendiceal disease," I said.

"History?" Cathy said.

"There you go," I said. "Spector?"

He shrugged.

I said, "Up until 1886 the term appendicitis, and the knowledge of its morbidity, was not in the texts. Abscesses in that area were lumped together under the term iliac passion. It's now been identified in the mummies of Egypt, and an Egyptian princess is reputed to have died of it."

Spector muttered, "If they had wanted us to know medical history it would have been included in med school."

"If God had wanted us to fly ... " I said.

"Maybe he did," Cathy said. "What else are pectoral muscles for?"

I looked sideways at her and didn't tell her.

"Appendicitis, its recognition as an entity," I said, "is another instance of authority holding back progress. A man named Melier in 1827 described five cases of perforation of the appendix causing death. The reigning surgeon of the time—and reigning then meant they had all the autocracy of kings—said that this was nonsense. And progress was held back for fifty years while people died. Reginal Fitz, of Harvard, described it in 1886. He was a pathologist. A doctor got sick, he thought he had this newly described disease, and he called in Fitz. Being examined by a pathologist, he said, was the dream of every doctor—to be present at his own autopsy."

"Hurray," Spector said.

"Education," I said. "You recognize McBurney's point, and you don't know who he was. McBurney's incision, coming in right over the appendix. You use it, and you don't question who he was. Or Murphy, the farm boy who settled in Chicago and first described the symptoms we all use today, central abdominal pain radiating to the right lower quadrant, nausea and vomiting."

"Personally," Cathy said, "I am not interested in history for its own sake. That's a hobby. I have other hobbies."

206

Women in surgery, I thought. Cathy was an exception. She was attractive. What I saw around me were women mostly with thick glasses and thick ankles and thick waists who, with stethoscopes dangling, participated in group discussions like everybody else only they wore skirts. They met hundreds of staff people, men, and were socially prominent and married other doctors.

"Spector," I said, "let Cathy do the appendix and you help, you teach her."

"No!" he almost yelped. "Why do you want to waste an appendix on her? She's not going to be a surgeon. She'll never do another one. She's going into public health or something. Sure, someday she might be in a submarine and there's an emergency appendectomy and she is the only doctor available. But I still say it's a waste."

"What do you mean I won't be a surgeon?" Cathy said. "I might decide to, how do you know? And don't be so superior. Women can do anything men can."

"As a doctor, I dispute that," I said.

"Medically," Cathy said.

"I never heard of a lady surgeon amounting to anything," Spector said. "I never read an important surgical paper by a woman. There were two female residents who started in this program. One got married, had six kids, and is working as an admitting physician doing screening in a V.A. hospital. The other is working one day a week at a student health clinic."

"Cry your heart out," Cathy said. "We're moving into a matriarchal society and you're not prepared for it."

"It's true," I said, "that women coming into surgery can be as technically capable as men. In addition they have certain additional advantages. For example, Cathy, you got more work from Fisher than any other student. Was it because you took advantage of your sex?"

"Of course not. It's true that I recognized he liked flattery and I flattered him and he gave me parts of a hernia and an amputation. But you wouldn't call that taking advantage of my sex."

"Of course not," I said. "I'm letting you do part of the appendix. The question is, would I have let Newman do it? Am I influenced by your blond hair and blue eyes and White Shoulders?"

"Dr. Schein, really. It's Joy."

207

Was I really going to let a medical student do part of an operation on my patient? Of course not. She would think she was doing it, she would wind up holding a few clamps, but the actual procedure would be done by me. Like putting a child on your lap and letting him think he was driving the car.

The attitude of some surgeons toward students is to let them do as much as they reasonably can, with the feeling that they cannot get into any trouble that the surgeon cannot get them out of. I, on the other hand, anticipate every possible misadventure that can occur to student fingers. ABC is my acronym in surgery. I tell it to students: always be careful.

"I really don't want her to get the idea that she can do it," Spector said. "It's dangerous to let a woman feel she is more capable than she actually is."

30

Cathy said, "I still have trouble with the idea of taking out a healthy appendix. You seem to be talking about preventive surgery, Dr. Schein, and I have never heard of that."

"Okay," I said. "The question seems to be whether taking out Padget's appendix can be termed unnecessary surgery. Unnecessary surgery is that procedure which is done for monetary gain, or out of ignorance, and through culpability. I would not, in this case, enlarge the incision or in any way add insult to what is presented. Here's the appendix in an unobstructed field and ready for two clamps and a cut and tie. And what would be gained? Padget will not get appendicitis. Nor will the appendix mimic intestinal problems coming from his former condition. The appendectomy is indicated, no question."

Spector said, "A patient without an appendix puts a heavy strain on a surgeon's diagnostic ability. He can't blame that organ. At least fifty conditions mimic appendicitis. In most cases the easiest way out is the way in. We're doing Padget, and any surgeon he goes to in the future, a favor."

"I'm just not conditioned to the removal of healthy tissue," Cathy said.

"All you're doing," I said, "is latching onto a phrase. In this business we have to make people better. That means we use what comes from our education, our experience, and, beyond that, our surgical intuition. What the old Germans say is the difference between *Wissen* and *Ahnung*. Some things you know from the textbooks. Some things you know from feeling."

"How do you learn that, feeling?" Spector said. "I don't have that."

"Why should you have it? You do fifty cases and you start to have it with the fifty-first. You meaning some surgeons. Fisher will never have it."

"I really would like a little," Spector said.

"First it took so long to recognize appendicitis as a disease," I said. "And now, having learned to cope with it, the damn thing is starting to disappear. In our lifetime we'll probably refer to it as a vanishing entity. But while it is still with us it continues to present all kinds of problems. Twenty percent of the time we have trouble diagnosing it at all. Especially in women, when the symptoms of appendicitis turn out to be salpingitis or a twisted ovary."

"I had one of those," Spector said. "I took out the appendix anyway."

"You too, Brutus?" Cathy said.

"Look, lady surgeon," Spector said. "There is very little risk in that incidental operation, you know that? Both published and personal, right, Dr. Schein?"

"Right," I said.

"I just thought of something," Cathy said. "Padget gets into trouble in the future, he shows all the symptoms of appendicitis, but it's due to something else. But he doesn't have a typical appendectomy scar."

"That's why he has to be told," I said. "And his immediate family has to be told. As it happens, any surgeon seeing the scar from this operation would ask about his appendix, since most surgeons today would do the incidental appendectomy."

"Most laymen think diagnosing appendicitis is not all that difficult," Cathy said. "It's one of those diseases that's so popular."

"Let me tell you two stories," I said. "One is about a man I know who could, without makeup, take part in any movie requiring a surgeon. Tall, distinguished, gray-haired, talks, looks, and walks like a surgeon. Interested in social causes, too, he makes speeches and the patients and the nurses love him. I used to watch him taking out appendices. How beautifully he worked, how neat, how precise. Then it occurred to me why his operations were always so perfect. He never had trouble because he rarely ran into a diseased appendix. They were all prefectly normal. The problem was usually gynecological. Luckily, the diseases were self-limiting, for the most part, or responded to antibiotic treatment. He worked in a large city

210

hospital where there were many instances of P.I.D.—pelvic inflammatory disease—and although operations were not required they were safer than not going in, because there was always the chance of missing a real perforated appendix."

"How did he feel, taking out all those normal appendices?" Cathy said.

"As far as I know, he felt great. In my case, if I go in for an appendix and find it normal, but in the course of the laparotomy I find a twisted ovarian cyst or intestinal obstruction, or a pelvic abscess, and I fix that along with taking out the appendix, then my original misdiagnosis isn't bad. Anyway, Cathy, you're entitled to the ignorance that goes with your social awareness, but you have no surgical experience and I really don't know why I'm bothering with you."

"What's the second story, Dr. Schein?" Cathy said, not insulted at all.

"Ah, yes. This involves a simple appendectomy I was doing with a resident. A resident, you hear me, Spector?"

"It wasn't me," he said.

"No. So how do we find an appendix? We look for the cecum, right? And what's attached to it, at any point of the clock, and that's why it's difficult, because at twelve o'clock it's up against the kidney and when inflamed it can simulate a kidney infection, and at three o'clock it can simulate an intestinal obstruction or green-apple colic or diarrhea, and at six o'clock it kisses the ovary and can simulate ovarian disease. Anyway, holding the cecum I pointed out the appendix and the resident took it out. I asked him if he was satisfied and he said yes. I asked him if he was perfectly satisfied and was ready to close. He said yes. I said, 'Stupid, what are you going to do with this adjacent cancer of the colon?' "

"Was he embarrassed?" Cathy said.

"Not at all. He was young enough to think himself infallible, evidence to the contrary notwithstanding."

"The moral is," Spector said, "that especially in an older person with appendicitis, one should always look for some associated disorder."

"Finally," I said. "There's hope for you yet, Spector."

"Experience is the name given to our past mistakes," he said smugly.

"How well I've taught you," I said. "When I go into the ward for rounds I tell the interns, Don't tell me what went right. Tell me about the screw-ups. An eighteen-year-old girl came into the emergency room with abdominal pain and the resident in charge diagnosed fecal impaction. Why was he wrong? Because most people have what most people have, and at eighteen, despite our eating habits and slothful lives, you don't see fecal impaction. She was sent home and came back twenty-four hours later with a ruptured appendix."

"I don't understand what you tell a patient after taking out a normal appendix," Cathy said.

"Oh, you again," I said. "There was a lady who had her appendix out—normal, Cathy, of course—and the doctor told her he took it out and she'd be all right. And then afterward she passed a kidney stone and naïvely inquired if that might not have been the sole cause of her trouble. The doctor, if honest, would have had to admit it."

"Did he?" Cathy said.

"Are we not all honorable men?" I said.

"When you're in private practice," Spector said, "as I hope to be as soon as I can escape from this madhouse, things look different. A friend of mine practicing in the boondocks where I hope to join him, told me of a general practitioner who had a neurotic patient who was bothering him with persistent bouts of presumed appendicitis which he insisted was in her head but she wore him down and finally he sent her to the surgeon saying, 'This lady at this point insists she has chronic appendicitis, and I can't talk her out of it and how do I know there isn't the off chance she might not be right?' So the surgeon, who wasn't doing anything that afternoon anyway, schedules her and she doesn't have anything except appendicitis of the brain, but the lady feels a lot better after the operation. Sometimes it's the patient. You can't yell unscrupulous surgeon every time."

"A lot of things look like appendicitis," I said. "We've made that point. Sometimes it can be tragic. Morning sickness in early pregnancy can mimic appendicitis. You can take out the appendix and sometimes get a miscarriage. She can get pregnant again, or maybe she didn't want the child in the first place. But there was a case of a lady who had not been able to get pregnant and wanted to

212

badly and the studies showed it was because she ovulated infrequently. One gynecologist followed this woman, taking temperatures, and after eighteen months of observation an ovulatory cycle was picked up and the husband was informed and impregnation took place. So you know the rest. The gynecologist left on vacation, the lady came down with severe abdominal pain, the diagnosis was possible appendicitis. The surgeon was informed of her pregnancy, and recognized the risk, but the decision was made. The appendix was normal and she miscarried, and has not been able to conceive again. So we're not, after all, gods. Godlike, yes."

"It's always the women who suffer," Cathy said.

"Enough foreplay," I said. "Now to the appendix."

"I thought we were still discussing that," Cathy said.

"Well," I said, "I see I have to tell you about the professor who ran the surgical chest conference when I was a medical student. At that time tuberculosis was treated by air installation, surgical collapse, or removing the diseased area. The professor, considering the choice of therapy with each case presented, would take a vote. 'How many for pneumo? Five. How many for thoracoplasty? Five. How many for excision? One. All right, we'll take the lung out.' But, you may ask, that was not the majority. True. In such ways do autocrats make democratic decisions in surgery."

"Where do you want me?" Spector said.

"You'll second assist. I'm going to let Cathy do this one."

"Really?" she said.

"Yes. You will take out this man's appendix."

I found the cecum and picked it up. "The three muscular layers here all meet at the base of the appendix. Which is your guide for finding it. You always go for the cecum first, the appendix follows. And behold, here it is."

Spector looked at me and winked. In excising an appendix the only difficulty is to find it. The appendix looks like a worm.

Cathy said, "Gee, he's got a long one."

"Notice," Spector said, "how I refuse to comment on that." I gave him the cecum to hold in a lap pad.

I held up the tip of the appendix with a Babcock clamp and gave it to Cathy. "Hold this in your left hand." She had the appendix extended. The mesentery showed up like the sail on a ship, the appendix was the mast. I perforated the mesentery where the clamp was to be applied to close off the blood vessel. "All right, Cathy, I'll let you apply this clamp, if you can tell me its name and whether the holding serrations on it are longitudinal or transverse. Two reasonable questions. Any plumber has to know something about his tools."

"Something Irish," Cathy said. "O'Toole?"

"Kelly. One wrong. And the other question?"

"I don't know how the serrations go."

"You're ignorant, so I can't let you put the clamp on."

"But, Dr. Schein, you said I could take out the appendix."

"And so you shall, my child."

I put a pair of clamps through the mesentery, controlling the blood vessels between its jaws. "All right, Cathy, cut between them."

She did, and I said, "Now to show you how you tie this." I used a chromic catgut to tie off the mesoappendix. The appendix was now attached only at its base.

"You're not letting me do anything, Dr. Schein."

"I said you're going to take it out."

I clamped off the base and cut and tied and the appendix dangled from the clamp Cathy was holding.

"There," I said. "Take it out, Cathy."

"You tricked me," she said, handing the organ to Rodriguez, who handed it to the circulating nurse, who put it in a bottle. There were three parts of Padget now lying side by side.

In a tray covered with a green towel was part of his stomach and his ulcer, and in a bottle the appendix, and in another bottle the severed portions of the vagus nerves.

"All Padget divided in three parts," Spector said.

"A classical education never hurt any surgeon," I said.

"And I'm supposed to say I took out his appendix?" Cathy said.

"Didn't you?" I said.

"I thought she did it very well," Spector said.

214

31

Spector said, "Well, Cathy, now that you're a surgeon you ought to know the association's ten commandments for residents. May I give them to her, Dr. Schein?"

"Sure. I want to see if you remember."

"Okay. One. Avoid offending those in power. Two. Recognize the wisdom and experience of your superiors. Three. Be firm only with those who are weaker than you. Four. Be prepared to switch allegiance from the declining ruler to the rising tyrant. Five. Do not rebut the lies of your superiors with the truth. Six. Let your superior choose where he wants his name on your paper. Seven. On controversial issues take a firm position in the middle. Eight. In power plays do not choose sides without a guarantee. Nine. Put nothing in writing. Ten. Don't get caught."

"There's another one," I said. "I didn't include it because Moses thought that ten was enough. Sometimes in order to succeed all you have to give up is your principles and self-esteem."

"Sure," Cathy muttered. "I took out his appendix, all right."

"How was the conference, Cathy?" I said.

"I'll tell you, Dr. Schein. It was an experience. Incidentally, Williams presented one of the cases very well."

And why not, I thought. She had come to me at my office. "Dr. Schein, I have to present a case at a conference."

"What conference?"

"That one being held by the staff for the doctors of the community. It's to be about abdominal pain, its diagnosis and treatment."

"Good," I said.

"What I'm doing is taking one of your cases, which is why I

215

came to you, and also because as my instructor in surgery I thought you could give me some advice."

What did it matter if I found this student dull and stupid? My job was to teach, was it not? Did I have to screen my students on the basis of intelligence and appearance before responding to them? My answer to myself was that I wished I could. My duty was another matter.

"Which case?" I said.

"Mrs. Garden?"

"Who's she?"

"The gallbladder."

"I've done more than a thousand."

"Well, it was the early part of the year, she was an elderly woman—"

"Now listen, Williams. First, particularize the woman so she can be remembered. She's the one who runs the corner luncheonette."

"Yes, that's the one."

"So you say that. To make her remembered."

She was taking notes. I wished, as I had wished many times before, that she had taken to law or homemaking. "Williams. Listen. Don't take notes. Listen. First, know the case so well that you don't need notes when you get up to present it. She had a history of gallbladder difficulty. She comes in with pain. We examine her. We test her. We take X rays. You state all this, giving only the positive results of the tests. You have the X rays in order and know just where the abnormalities are. You put yourself in the place of the audience and anticipate possible questions they will ask. You speak in a clear loud voice that can reach to the end of the conference room."

"I get nervous, Dr. Schein. I have a small voice."

"Go to the conference hall with a friend in advance of your presentation and let her sit in the back row and practice. Being successfully extemporaneous means to be well rehearsed."

"What was that, Dr. Schein?"

"Never mind. Be an actor. Surgeons are natural actors. Tell a joke."

"I don't know any jokes."

"Learn one. And you will notice that there will be rude people

216

in the audience. Somebody will be smoking a cigar and talking to a friend. Somebody might be reading the newspaper. Concentrate on them, be so interesting and informed that they will listen."

"I don't know if I can do that, Dr. Schein."

"Of course you can, Williams. Above all, remember that you know more about this case than anybody there. You're the expert."

"So Williams did all right?" I said to Cathy.

"Yes. She even told a joke."

"Did anybody laugh?"

"I did."

The surgical conference. There were guest speakers. I was often one. It was a break in routine, you were granted the respect of your position; sometimes you even had something new to say. The local practitioners listen, and sometimes learn something. I remember looking at them from the platform and developing an acute sense of separateness. They saw people in their cage or castle.

I rarely made house calls, but I remember one. An old lady alone sitting on a faded velvet couch with antimacassars on the back and arms. There were photographs of relatives on the living-room table. I examined her and she needed attention but I doubted that it was surgical. What she needed was companionship. And I got a feeling of being on an express train, rushing as far and as fast as I could from that room, from that lonely old lady, the patient.

I looked at my colleagues and I made a list.

The I-saved-your-life surgeon. "If it had gone on for another fifteen minutes, if it had gone an incher deeper—" He throws up his hands and rolls his eyes heavenward.

The gifted, careless one. He puts in his thumb where he shouldn't and says, "Oops! Just like the last time."

The saintly surgeon who relied on nature more than God intended. He was so angelic that patients apologized to him for their complications.

The austere, detached surgeon who never had a complication. When reminded that one of his patients on the fourth postoperative day threw himself out the window he said. "Well, he was fine when he left the hospital."

The one who relies on luck. In an emergency he closes his eyes and steps on the gas.

217

The academician who knows all the footnotes and very little of the text.

The journeyman who is devoted to his family and surgery is as good a way to make a living as any other.

The assassin.

The unlucky one. His patients get every complication known, and some previously undescribed.

The naysayer. Prepared in advance for everything to be hopeless.

The businessman. During the conferences he shuffles bills.

The plodder. The cases have to be simple.

The regional specialist. Knows everything in all languages about one minute area.

The slovenly one. His surgery is even more disordered than his appearance.

The husband. His wife knows more about his practice than he does. Knows all his referring doctors by their first names and invites them to dinner parties. Knows the birthdays of all their wives. Says, "We had a tough case last week."

The fatalist. If his patients don't recover it's not his fault.

The one who is reminded. Whatever comes up he is reminded of his own case. He has one for all aspects of all surgical problems.

The one who doesn't read the journals. Still does uterine suspensions for female backaches. Relies on his resident to bring him up to date.

The hallway consultant. Catches you in the corridor and asks about his problems in an informal way. Never asks you to see the patient.

The one who says, "Boy, I've got an X ray you'd like to see." Actually, I don't want to see it. He wants me to see it.

The purveyor of good will. He shakes his pelt at you and you step back not wanting to be sprayed.

The mechanical genius who should have stayed with cars.

The Olympian from Texas.

The sufferer. Agonizes with his patients over their misfortunes, usually attributable to his own errors.

The one who has lost interest in surgery and can't admit it.

The compassionate surgeon who will forgive you anything but your success.

218

The schlemiel. He knocks over I.V. stands and refers to the patient's wife as his mother.

The silent one. Has no knowledge on which to base an opinion and doesn't want to be misquoted.

"So tell me about the conference, Cathy. What did you get from it?"

"What I noticed," Cathy said, "was their hostility."

"Hostility?"

"Sure. All the surgeons sat around talking to one another but not because they liked each other, but because they happened to be in the same business."

"You felt that? How could you feel that?"

"*Ahnung,*" Cathy said. "Everybody there was competitive. And hostile. Did I say that before, hostile?"

"Yes, you did. But why hostile?"

"At all levels. Competition for the patient, competition for the feeder of patients. The specialist surgeon against the general surgeon because the generalist does what he does. Those who teach against those who practice. Those who are salaried against those in private practice."

"How could you know all that, Cathy? You're just a young student, you don't understand. But what did you learn about abdominal pain? That's what you were there for."

"I didn't learn anything I didn't know before. And if there were things I might have learned I didn't understand the language. I didn't even know the names of some of the procedures they were talking about."

"Well, you're not a surgeon yet, Cathy, even though you've taken out an appendix."

"I'm a student, I went there to learn. Even if it wasn't a conference for students there should have been more there for me to learn. They got so damned detailed. As if they were vying with each other to show off the jargon."

"That's not fair. You don't understand something and you call it intentional professional obfuscation."

"Is that what I call it? I think the purpose of language is to communicate."

"They were communicating with their peers."

"Really, Dr. Schein, I looked at the people there and saw remnants of the lithotomist, barber surgeon, bathouse keeper, wigmaker, wound dresser, and the rest of the characters from the medical history you made me read. I wanted to be impressed, Dr. Schein, I really did, and it seemed to me the doctors there were more interested in revealing their own astuteness than in participating in a mutual effort to make themselves better doctors."

"You're not fair," I said.

"I've heard you say things like this about your colleagues before."

"Then I wasn't fair. The truth is these people, these surgeons, despite their imperfections, are a cut above the ordinary man. Look what they've gone through.

"College and medical school. Then the rigorous requirements to become a surgeon, and all of them—I mean all of them, the ones I despise as well as those I revere—have one thing in common. They all share a desire to learn as much as possible, and to be able to utilize the information in the treatment of patients. A doctor, if he could, would be all-knowing. That's the common desire. The differences lie in the willingness to devote the time and energy and sacrifices knowledge requires, and differences in capacity to apply it. One gets out in the world and finds deforming and contrary stresses—the need to make a living, to get along with one's wife, to raise children, the fatigue factor added to age, and the loss of a sense of our own immortality. Surgeons get ulcers and sometimes don't survive the disease they've cured in their patients. Surgery can be a way in life, or a way of life. And the decisions are not always under one's control. So, Cathy, be tolerant."

"I need someone to pattern myself after, don't I? Doesn't a student need someone to emulate? Who shall I choose?"

"What's wrong with taking a little from each? You can't, really, be a bad person and a good surgeon. I believe that."

"I went to that meeting expecting a surgical conference," Cathy said. "You know what I found, a bunch of people talking about surgery."

"That's what we are," I said. "People."

220

32

We were ready to close Padget's abdomen. A number of things could go wrong here—as, of course, a number of things might have gone wrong during the operation itself. What we did now could shorten or interfere with Padget's immediate recovery, or could be the cause of later difficulty. So you exercise the care which has been ingrained through rote. Now there was no place for intuition.

I wanted complete relaxation of the abdominal wall. To test it, I took four clamps and grasped the peritoneum, one on either end of the incision and one on either side of the center. I lifted the two ends to see if the peritoneum would raise easily with nothing adhering. If we tried to suture a tight belly the stitches could pull through.

"Everything all right?" I asked Patel.

"Fine. Enough relaxation?"

"Yes. Keep him right here. Don't let him buck." Which meant cough: I couldn't have him in spasm while I was sewing.

I asked Rodriguez for a lap-pad count. So many to start with, the same number to finish with. If we were short any I had to look for them in the abdomen. It was not all that impossible to forget one. "Spector," I said, "this is the time to be extra careful. And you can't depend on the nurses alone for a count. Get your hand in and feel around. We leave a pad in and the lawyers descend like buzzards. And according to law—the doctrine is *respondeat superior*—which means let the master answer, which means you, the surgeon, are the captain, and as such responsible for everything that can go wrong."

Satisfied with the count and the check by hand I placed the abdominal curtain, the omentum, back in place between the ab-

221

dominal wall and the bowel. Then I began to sew up the peritoneum.

Cathy said, "Dr. Schein, I have a question I probably have no right to ask."

"Then I probably have no need to answer. But go ahead."

"What is your fee going to be for this operation?"

I have never asked anyone that question. It was a little startling coming from a student. But maybe it was a question that ought to be asked more often.

"What would you charge?" I said.

"I can't answer that. I have no experience."

"Would you believe, Cathy," I said, "that with all the experience I do have, I still don't really know what to charge? It's a damned ticklish business.

"Take the patient. He gets sick. He didn't ask to get sick, it wasn't his fault, he loses time from his job and there's all that anxiety and trauma and on top of that some doctor is asking him to pay an enormous fee. Now that's not right. Add to the inequities the fact that health insurance pays the hospital in full, but only a fraction of the doctor's bill."

As I sewed the peritoneum, with each run of four or five suture passes I put my hand in to see that the undersurface was free.

"So, Cathy. More aspects of the fee situation. It has always been traditional that medical fees vary. The poor used to pay nothing, the rich what the traffic bore. Meanwhile, let's look at the patient's viewpoint. The Latin poem sees the doctor as three beings—an angel when he first appears, a god when he cures you, and a devil when he sends his bill."

Over the peritoneal suture the rectus muscles slid back into place. I started to sew up the fascial envelope which enclosed it, using interrupted nonabsorbable sutures. As I put the thread in Spector grabbed each end and knotted it. Eight throws for each.

"Let me tell you the old story about the chicken bone, Cathy. You know it?"

"No."

"If you're ever going to be a practicing physician you ought to know it. A man comes in to a doctor hardly able to talk or breathe, in panic, a chicken bone caught in his throat. The doctor reaches in and with one deft motion removes the bone. The man sighs in relief and then demands, Hey, Doc, what are you going to charge me for

222

that? Half as much, says the doctor, as you were willing to pay two minutes ago."

"So what's your fee going to be?" Cathy said.

"I'm coming to that. The nature of the operation determines the reaction to your fee. If you cure a man of stomach ulcer, if he now can eat with enjoyment and remembers his preoperative pain and nausea, he will pay your fee and be grateful besides. It's hard to pay a fee gratefully if the operation was removal of a leg or a breast. Incidentally, Cathy, the one operation for which patients are delighted to pay is when you remove a benign tumor of the breast. They send you other patients. You rarely get a referral from a patient who has had a mastectomy.

"Then some patients want to know how long the operation took and gauge the fee accordingly, thinking the man who took four hours is more worthy of a stiffer fee than one who took one hour, when in truth the one hour operation may have been performed by the more expert of the two and what he was charging for was the twenty years it took him to learn how to do it. Insurance companies determine their fees according to a standard. A standard operation performed by a standard surgeon. But what if you're above average, more competent, more imaginative, just generally better. In any other field you get more money for being better. But insurance companies don't recognize this."

"What are you going to charge Mr. Padget?" Cathy said.

"One final word about the reaction of patients to the fee. It's a question of confidence. One of the most incompetent people we have on the staff charges the highest fees and his patients love to pay it. He has all sorts of postoperative problems which he has himself caused by his poor work in the operating room and they love him, he fights so hard to save their lives. And then there is the story of the lady with the bronchoscopy."

Spector said, "Let me add one thing. As time passes no woman will remember the name of the surgeon who operated on her. Yet she will always remember the name of the doctor who delivered her first child."

"Okay," Cathy said. "You blank out everything connected with an unhappy experience. But I want to get to the question of fees."

We were ready now for the skin. I said to Spector, "You start at the top, let Cathy begin at the bottom. I'll watch."

"He's throwing you the classic bone," Spector said. "It's interesting, though, that the cosmetic part of the operation, the only part the patient sees, is relegated to the student."

"Hey," I said, "I'm watching. If it isn't done properly I'll yell."

"And," Cathy said, "the patient often judges the operation by the condition of the scar."

"Thus," I said, "proving my confidence in you."

"What about the bronchoscopy?" Cathy said, using a straight needle threaded with black silk.

"Yes. We are talking about confidence. I used to be a member of a medical group. Patients prepaid and were individually treated for their problems without further fee. We had a lady who had been spitting up blood, the X rays were negative, and the bronchoscopy was indicated to inspect the bronchi and lungs. An appointment was made but the lady didn't show up, subsequently explaining that she had not made up her mind about the procedure. A week later I received a patient in my private office. I thought she looked familiar. She brought an X ray and gave me her history and she said she had been told she needed a bronchoscopy. At that point I recognized her, and I told her I was the same doctor she had seen at the group. She said something about not knowing I was a real specialist, and she then said it was her habit always to get a second opinion. I told her she now had the same opinion twice, if from the same doctor. A matter of image. A matter of confidence."

While Spector was sewing I said, "Paul, let's go over the postop orders."

"Routine for gastrectomy," he said.

"Let's check them anyway," I said, putting the patient's welfare higher than the resident's sensitivity.

"We'll check his blood pressure, pulse, and respiration every fifteen minutes until he's stabilized. We'll give him something for pain every four hours. We'll continue to feed him I.V. with glucose and vitamins. We'll check his hematocrit to make sure of his blood volume and measure his urinary output every hour to see he's perfusing properly. And we'll keep his nasogastric tube open by intermittent irrigation. Anything else?"

"No, Paul, that's fine."

With the skin closed I took off the drapes and threw them into a laundry hamper. Spector dried off the skin, Cathy put on a bandage, and Spector applied adhesive tape. The anesthetist and an

224

orderly got Padget onto a bed for transfer to the recovery room. I stripped off gown and gloves and went out to the hall and got some orange juice from the refrigerator. Cathy, behind me, said, "You're not going to give me a figure on that fee, are you?"

"No. That's part of the doctor-patient relationship, isn't it? Of course, you might ask Padget. He's also your patient, Cathy. Keep an eye on him. The operation was only one phase of his treatment. He'll be here for another ten days."

I went out and the girl at the desk said, "Dr. Schein, the Padget family is waiting for you."

I thought what a chore it was, this need to see the family after each operation. But I remember that once, coming out of the O.R., the information clerk did not tell me the family was waiting, and I asked why, and she said that nobody was waiting, and I thought how sad it was that no one cared about that patient. So I went to talk to Padget's wife and high school daughter.

"Mrs. Padget," I said at once, "he's fine. The operation went well. I took out his ulcer, I also took out his appendix. Nothing unusual."

She had bright-red dyed hair, rings on each finger, too much makeup. I wondered if I were looking at Padget's ulcer. She said, "Well, I'm glad that's over."

The daughter thanked me.

I was hungry, but it was more than an hour before lunchtime.

I went back toward the locker room and the clerk stopped me. "Dr. Schein, your office called. They asked that you look in at the emergency room as soon as you're finished here. Dr. Jordan sent over a patient with a perforated ulcer."

Postscript

Williams is associated with a well-known neurosurgeon in Arkansas.

Fisher is writing a book, but hasn't decided on the subject.

Cathy Forge is practicing radiology in a university town near Denver.

Padget is alive, divorced, and well.

Today both Spector and Newman also are surgeons at work.